MODEL STATIONARY AND
MARINE STEAM ENGINES

MODEL

STATIONARY AND MARINE

STEAM ENGINES

K. N. HARRIS

MODEL & ALLIED PUBLICATIONS
ARGUS BOOKS LIMITED
Station Road, Kings Langley,
Hertfordshire, England

Model and Allied Publications,
Argus Books Limited,
Station Road, Kings Langley,
Hertfordshire, England

First published 1958

Second Edition 1964

Second Impression 1969

Third Impression 1972

Fourth Impression (paperback) 1974

Fifth Impression (paperback) 1975

ISBN 0 85344 072 7

Printed in Great Britain
By Unwin Brothers Limited
The Gresham Press, Old Woking, Surrey England
A member of the Staples Printing Group.

CONTENTS

FIGURES

PLATES

INTRODUCTION

IN A small handbook of this size, it is quite impossible to deal at all comprehensively with what is, in fact, a very large subject. The course adopted is to attempt to explain, as simply as possible, first principles, and to follow up with a series of practical designs, ranging upwards from the very simplest, which themselves serve to illustrate the more important types that have been in use over the last one hundred years.

It is well at the outset for the reader to appreciate certain important facts about model steam engines in general; for a number of years now there has been a strong and growing tendency for the impression to arise that the model steam engine, particularly the model locomotive, is more efficient than is the full-sized prototype. This is a gross travesty of fact.

The very best full size reciprocating steam engines are themselves far from being thermally efficient, and models of them become progressively less efficient as their scale size diminishes. All model steam engines are, on the thermal side, most inefficient, even the best of them, and nobody who has the most elementary knowledge of thermo-dynamics would expect anything else. Practical power tests carried out under properly controlled and independently observed conditions amply confirm this statement; the fundamental reasons which underly this inefficiency will be explained in Chapter 1.

I hope, however, nobody will be led away by the specious argument that as the average model engine consumes, comparatively speaking, so little fuel, efficiency is not worth worrying about. That seems to me the absolute antithesis of the spirit of the true model engineer. Carrying that argument a little further, why bother to build model engines at all ! As I see it it comes to this, if you are a true model engineer you will strive for the greatest efficiency you can achieve and nothing less will (or should) satisfy you; the old saying that " A thing worth doing is worth doing well " applies with full force to model steam engine building, and " doing well " includes getting the most efficient performance you can obtain from your engine.

I am not so foolish as to claim to have unique or exclusive knowledge about steam engines large or small, but I spent the first twenty years of my working life helping to build and erect them, later installing, testing, and maintaining them, and later still designing them. On the model side, I have been building them for over fifty years, so that I can at least claim to have had a fairly extensive practical experience of the subject. I make no claim either that my own beliefs are infallible or incapable of being improved upon, merely that they are the fruit of not inconsiderable experience and study.

The model stationary engine has for a number of years been badly neglected, which is a pity. The beginner who gets bitten with the urge to build a 3½ in. or 5 in. gauge four cylinder " Pacific " locomotive, would be well advised before embarking on such a project, first to make one or two simple stationary engines. He will learn a great deal from their construction and operation which will be of the greatest value to him when he gets around to the putting into effect of his model locomotive aspirations ; above all, he will have brought home to him in no uncertain manner the immense amount of work involved in building a fairly large and complicated locomotive. Look through the columns of advertisements of second-hand goods for sale, in the model engineering press, and you will find that they are liberally besprinkled with offers of " part-finished " model locomotives of every sort, size, and description, from " O " gauge to 2 in. scale; they are very largely the unfinished attempts of people whose ambition has outrun their skill or patience, or the gullible ones led away by the pernicious and sedulously fostered idea that " everything is quite easy if the instructions are followed."

If these people had only tackled a simple job to start with, they would have been much more likely to finish the more ambitious one later. Ambition is a fine thing, but it wants liberally mixing with common sense, a realistic outlook and a sense of proportion.

In conclusion, it is not my intention to make more use of figures and formulae than is necessary, but, for an *intelligent* understanding of the steam engine, some elementary knowledge of simple arithmetic is essential, and some figures and formulae must be used to establish and explain fundamental facts. There is no one " best way " of doing any particular job, it depends on circumstances such as the skill and experience (or lack of it !) of the individual concerned, his equipment and his personal idiosyncrasies, and no one can lay down a set of instructions which will be of universal application.

If model engineering is to progress, no rational man will contest the fact that it will do so best and most rapidly by the greatest number of people understanding basic principles and exercising their brains and ingenuity and interchanging their ideas; not by huge numbers building up kit sets, or working to cut and dried instructions. If this little book helps in any way to that most desirable end, it will have achieved its purpose.

Finally, the model steam engine, as we know it today, in all its various forms, locomotive, traction, portable, marine, stationary, pumping, etc., etc., is not the product of any single individual super genius, or of any small and exclusive group, but is the result of the work of many enthusiasts over many years. Perhaps the greatest contributors have been the late Henry Greenly and the late Henry Muncaster, but there have been many others, all honour to all of them.

K. N. HARRIS.

INTRODUCTION TO SECOND EDITION

VERY LITTLE alteration has been found necessary to the text of the first edition; an error on page 77 of the edition in question, in the disc drain valve drawing, has been corrected and an additional type of single cock drain valve is illustrated. In the same chapter another useful form of governor, the Hartnall, is illustrated. Some additional data on feed pumps has been included together with details of two types, a long-stroke pump and a short-stroke pump.

Three new engine designs have been added, one an oscillating engine with a plate distributing valve, a type which comes between the simple one in which the moving of the cylinder provides the valve motion, and in consequence makes it impossible to obtain early cut-off or release, and the very much more complicated type used in full-size marine practice, in which the inlet and exhaust steam passed through the trunnions upon which the cylinder swung and an ordinary slide valve was operated either by a slip eccentric or a Stephenson link motion, through an ingenious arrangement which obviated the motion of the cylinder effecting the motion of the valve.

The second design is a launch engine, the original of which I designed for my employers more than fifty years ago, and the 3 in. scale model of which won the Championship Cup in the General Mechanical Models Class and the Bradbury-Winter Cup at the Model Engineer Exhibition in January, 1960. Both are illustrated by photographs.

The third design is not for a model at all, but for a small power twin non-condensing launch engine large enough to drive a full-sized launch. This is included as, although not a model, it can be built by any competent model engineer possessing a good back-geared lathe of not less than $3\frac{1}{2}$ in. centres (which brings it into the scope of the popular Myford ML7 or " Super.") In passing a half-size version would make an excellent hard working model, capable of driving a hull of from 6 to 10 ft. in length, depending on the type, say a 6 ft. tug or a 10 ft. liner.

Finally a chapter has been added on condensing and condensers, a branch of model engineering which, so far as stationary engine work (and even marine work too) is concerned, has been badly neglected.

It is hoped that these additions by giving a wider scope to the book will add both to its interest and practical utility.

A long chapter has been added on cylinder design and construction as it was felt that this vital matter was deserving of fuller treatment than was accorded to it in the original edition. The boiler is the source of power or, more strictly speaking, the fire in the boiler, and the cylinder provides the means of converting this power into useful work. Boilers are, comparatively speaking, efficient, engines not ; for that reason alone every endeavour should be made to see that the most vital part of the engine is both designed and made as efficiently as possible. Poor design and workmanship here can lead to a considerable augmentation of avoidable inefficiency.

The matter on governors has been much expanded and now constitutes a separate chapter.

K.N.H.

Kingscote Bros. & Williams 3 in. by 2 in. dynamo driving engine with shaft governor, built by the author

CHAPTER 1

FUNDAMENTAL PRINCIPLES OF WORKING

THERE ARE many people who believe that " Nature cannot be scaled "; but the truth is that with certain reservations nature can be " scaled " and is being scaled every day and all day, over the world by people who know their job.

If this statement were true, such things as ship testing tanks, wind tunnels, harbour and estuary models, to say nothing of a very large proportion of the work carried on at the National Physical Laboratory and similar establishments all over the globe, would be utterly useless and a complete waste of time, money, and human endeavour.

Certainly nature cannot be scaled on the delightful principle of simple proportion, but scaled it can be by any person of reasonable education and intelligence. If someone says " I cannot scale nature," one will accept this as fact ; if he says " nature cannot be scaled," he is simply making a statement which does not accord with plain, ascertainable fact.

Let us look at the matter by way of a practical illustration.

First look at the problem in its most elementary form. Consider a block of metal 12 in. cube, weighing 720 lb. This will have a volume of 1,728 cu. in., an exposed area of its six sides of 864 sq. in., and a weight as we have specified of 720 lb. Now we make an exact model of this to 1/12 linear scale. Its *linear* dimensions will obviously be 1/12 those of the original, its areas or surface dimensions will, however, only be 1/144 of those of the original, whilst its volumetric and weight dimensions will only be 1/1,728 of those of the original. Briefly, linear dimensions in any structure vary directly as the scale. Surfaces or areas vary as the square of the scale and volumes or weights as the cube of the scale. Thus each of its sides will measure 1 in. long as against 12 in. = 1/12 in the original. The area of each of its sides will be 1 sq. in., as against 144 sq. in. ($= 1/12^2$) of the original. Its volume will be 1 cu. in., as against 1,728 cu. in. ($= 1/12^3$) of the original and its weight will be 6 2/3 oz., or 1/1,728 of the original.

1

Let us apply these facts to the case of an engine.

Suppose we have a steam engine having a cylinder 12 in. bore by 24 in. stroke, and a boiler supplying it with steam having a heating surface of 144 sq. ft. (purely arbitrary figures, by the way) and working at 100 lb. per sq. inch pressure.

We propose to make a model exactly 1/12 linear scale. This will have a cylinder 1 in. bore × 2 in. stroke and the boiler will have a heating surface of 1 sq. foot.

Now the full sized engine has a swept cylinder volume of 113 × 24 cu. in. = 2,712 cu. in. so the heating surface ratio is 144/2,712 say, 0·053.

The model will have a swept cylinder volume of 0·785 × 2 = 1·570 cu. in., so the heating surface ratio here is 1/1·570 = 0·636, or just twelve times as great as in the full sized job.

Thus we find that our model relative to its cylinder size has 12 times the heating surface of the full sized job. Well may " a scale-size boiler steam a scale-size cylinder." Under such conditions it can hardly be a matter of wonder or for surprise that a scale-size boiler will steam a scale-size cylinder. The effects of this elementary scale law are felt right through model steam engineering.

If you require primarily a relatively efficient *working* model, it will depart from exact scale in many fundamental dimensions. There are two main divisions in model steam engines: (*a*) those intended primarily to do a job of work, such as driving a boat, a dynamo, or a pump, etc.; (*b*) perfect scale replicas of some full-size prototype.

This book is concerned purely with the former, and from what has already been said, it will be immediately apparent that this type of model, to give of its best, must be designed with a view to its intended purpose with knowledge of and regard to the laws governing its functioning. This, of course, applies to any machine or structure required to do a job of work, whether it is a sausage machine, a typewriter, a steam engine, or a bridge, but it is a fact that is frequently either completely ignored or just not understood. A full appreciation of these elementary facts will enable the designer and constructor of model steam engines to approach his problems as a realist.

Properties of Steam. This is obviously not the place for an exhaustive thesis on the thermo-dynamics of the steam engine, but it is essential to an intelligent approach to the subject, that the would-be designer and builder should understand certain fundamental facts regarding the production of steam, and its properties.

First as to units of measurement. In Britain, the accepted measurement of quantity of heat is the British Thermal Unit.

Basically this is the amount of heat necessary to raise the temperature of 1 lb. of water 1 deg. F.

The root source of power in a steam engine is not of course the steam, but the heat given up by the coal, oil, spirit, charcoal, or whatever fuel you are burning. Heat and energy are, in theory at least, interchangeable, and the boiling of water to produce steam is merely a convenient means of converting the heat given up by the fuel into energy.

One British Thermal Unit would, in perfect conditions, produce 778 ft. lb. of energy, i.e., enough energy to lift a weight of 778 lb. 1 foot, or 1 lb. 778 ft., or any combination giving a result of 778 ft. lb. Note particularly that the factor of time does not enter into this at all.

To raise the temperature of 1 lb. of water from, say, 62 deg. F. to 212 deg. F. (boiling point at normal atmospheric pressure) requires the input of (212 − 62) B.T.U. = 150 B.T.U., but having raised this pound of water to boiling point we have to put in a further 970 B.T.U. to convert it to steam ; this latter quantity is known as latent heat of vaporisation.

The total heat in one pound of steam at atmospheric pressure is 1,151 B.T.U.

To raise the pressure to 25 lb. above atmosphere requires an input of a further 21 B.T.U., whilst pressure of 50 lb. and 100 lb. above atmosphere require additions of still a further 10 B.T.U. and 22 B.T.U. respectively.

For a moment let us consider fuel, and we will take coal as our example. One pound of good Welsh steam coal will produce around 14,000 B.T.U. when completely burnt.

We already know that each B.T.U. is in theory, capable of producing 778 ft. lb. of work, therefore, there is in our pound of coal 14,000 × 778 ft. lb. of work available (that presumes a perfect boiler and a perfect engine). This equals 10,892,000 ft. lb. Now for a moment we must consider horse-power. Long ago this was established at the (largely arbitrary) figure of 33,000 ft. lb. of work per min., which equals 1,980,000 ft. lb. of work per hour.

We have seen that our pound of coal contains 10,892,000 ft. lb. of work, so that converting, we find that one pound of coal should produce about $5\frac{1}{2}$ h.p. for one hour.

In actual fact a good reciprocating marine steam plant will produce 1 h.p. per hour for a consumption of about $1\frac{1}{2}$ lb. of coal, which, in theory, should produce $8\frac{1}{4}$ h.p.

Thus the thermal efficiency in this case is about 12 per cent. As a further instance the thermal efficiency of the best steam locomotives is only 10 per cent. to 11 per cent.

Considering the steam itself, what happens when it is used in a steam engine cylinder? Assuming it to be saturated, i.e., at the same temperature as the water in the boiler, the moment it gets into the cylinder it loses heat through the cylinder walls. It has, in fact, already lost some heat on its way to the cylinder; this loss of heat can only be made good by some of the steam condensing and giving up its latent heat and this condensed portion is wasted. Further, it is usual to cut off the supply of steam before the piston reaches the end of its stroke in order to make use of its expansive properties. The moment it starts to expand however, it loses more heat and the condensation trouble is still further aggravated. The expansion does work, work and heat are interchangeable, so heat is lost, or rather converted.

If, however, steam previous to being used is superheated, that is, has further heat added to it in a vessel or series of tubes separated from the boiler, much of this condensation trouble is overcome; the steam has available some heat which it can give up *without condensing*, and the higher the superheat the more this will be.

As a general rule it pays to work at the highest pressure and the highest superheat that circumstances will allow.

Finally, let us briefly consider horse-power and the method of calculating it. As previously stated, 1 h.p. = 33,000 foot pounds of work per minute.

The formula for calculating the theoretical h.p. of an engine is as follows:

$$\frac{P \times L \times A \times N}{33,000} = 1 \text{ h.p.}$$

Where P = Mean effective pressure in cylinder.
L = Stroke of piston in feet.
A = Area of piston in sq. in.
N = Number of strokes per min. in a double acting engine.

Note particularly that P is *not* the boiler pressure, it is always less, frequently much less. First there are pipe and passage losses between boiler and cylinder, then there are condensation losses. If the steam is cut off before the end of the piston travel, the average pressure is still further reduced by expansion. Finally, there is the back pressure on the other side of the piston caused in getting rid of the exhaust.

As a very rough guide, in a small engine, say up to 1 in. or 1¼ in. bore cylinder, cutting off at ¾ stroke, P might be taken at 0.5 boiler pressure. Again the horse-power worked out by the formula takes no account of frictional losses in the engine, in other words of the engine's mechanical efficiency. These, too, in small sizes are likely to be comparatively large, and the useful horse-power the engine can give out at its shaft is not likely to be more than two-thirds of the calculated indicated horse-power, which is, of course, the work actually being done in the cylinder itself, not what appears at the crankshaft.

It is frequently stated that the loadings and stresses in a model are " much greater " than those in the prototype. That is the exact contrary of the actual facts in nearly every case.

Let us revert to our full size and model engines. In the first place model steam engines are almost always worked at lower boiler pressures than are the originals.

In the case under consideration the model would probably not be worked at over 50-60 lbs. ; let us accept the latter figure.

To start with then the pressure per sq. in. of piston area in our model will only be six-tenths of that of the original ; assuming perfect scale proportions all through, the stresses, strains, and bearing loads in the model will all be in this same reduced proportion. Furthermore, the stresses set up by inertia and centrifugal forces in the model will be enormously less than their equivalents in the full size job.

Again it has often been asserted that a boiler made accurately to scale would not stand a reasonable pressure for a model. This too, is just fantastic nonsense. To take an instance, suppose we make an exact 1 in. scale model of a Scotch marine boiler, the original of which worked at 200 lb. per sq. in. pressure, and that we use materials in its construction identical with those used in the prototype, then assuming our workmanship to be satisfactory, not only will this boiler be perfectly safe for a working pressure for a model, say, 100 lb. per sq. in., but it would be perfectly safe to work at the 200 lb. of the original. There are many and excellent reasons for not making exact scale models of boilers when they are required to work, complication and corrosion are two most obvious ones, lack of strength is very definitely not one.

It may be thought that this chapter is unduly long and technical, but I do feel that for the model engineer who has any ambition to become other than a pure copyist, it is absolutely essential that he should get a firm grasp of the fundamental laws and principles of the matter. They have only been sketched in here, but text books on the steam engine are easy to come by and will fill in all the missing points ; I strongly recommend the enthusiast to study a good one, such as Ripper or Rankine.

CHAPTER 2

OSCILLATING ENGINES

ALMOST EVERYBODY who is in the least interested in model steam engines must be familiar with the oscillating engine, for it has been made and sold in various forms of toy and model engines for years. It is by many regarded rather contemptuously as being fit only for toy purposes. This is largely due to the number of cheap and crude engines of this type made by the toy trade over the last sixty years; in this particular case the toy engines of fifty years ago were much better than their counterparts of today. In small sizes, for small powers, the simple oscillating engine has much in its favour. It is simple in action, has a minimum of moving parts, and if properly designed and made is extremely reliable over long periods.

The first set of drawings, Fig. 1, show complete details of a very simple single acting oscillating engine, $\frac{3}{8}$ in. bore, $\frac{3}{4}$ in. stroke, suitable for boat driving. Such an engine would drive a light hull of fine lines of 30 in. or more length, quite satisfactorily.

There are certain points to watch in all oscillating engines of this general type. It is most important that the cylinder port face should be truly parallel with the axis of the bore and that the pivot pin should be set on a line cutting through this axis and itself at right angles to the cylinder port face.

It is equally important that the fixed steam block port face should be at right angles to the axis of the crankshaft in both horizontal and vertical planes and that the hole for the pivot pin should be truly parallel with the axis of the crankshaft and a good fit on the pivot pin. The method of setting out the ports is indicated on the drawing and is common to both single and double acting engines of this type. Care must be exercised to get both cylinder port face and steam block face dead flat and the final stages of this are, for the less highly skilled at any rate, best achieved by reversing the usual order of things and rubbing the job on the face of a smooth file. Note that the portions near the pivot pin should always be " relieved " or cut away to avoid contact; this is a most important point.

Fig. 2 shows another engine of superior design, but involving more difficult work. This was designed by the late Harry Wedge and

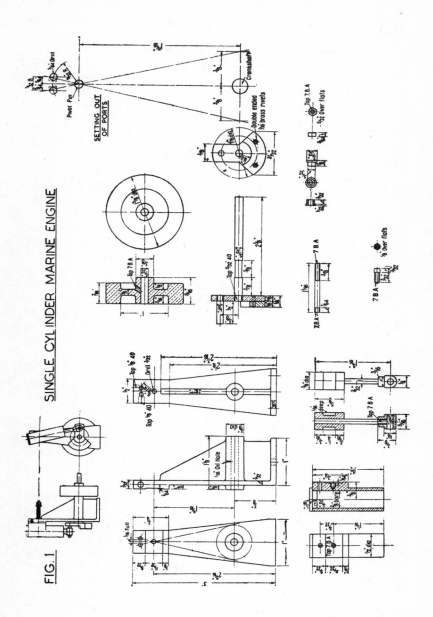

SINGLE CYLINDER MARINE ENGINE

FIG. 1

is an excellent example of what a little engine of this type can be when designed by an engineer and not just mass-produced on the cheapest possible lines.

The extension guide to the crosshead is an excellent feature; incidentally this is by no means new and can be seen in slightly different mechanical form on at least one engine in the Science Museum. Fig. 2 shows the engine exactly as Wedge designed it, whilst Fig. 2A shows certain small detail amendments which include a more substantial pivot pin and more efficient cylinder and steam-block porting.

Fig. 3 shows a more advanced and powerful engine of the same general type. This is a double acting engine with crosshead guide and a uniflow auxiliary exhaust port. A number of experiments I made some years ago indicate that this auxiliary exhaust port very definitely serves to pep up the engine performance at high speeds, whilst at the same time it adds no moving parts whatever.

This engine, which has a cylinder $\frac{5}{8}$ in. bore by $\frac{3}{4}$ in. stroke would drive a fine lined hull of anything up to 4 ft. 0 in. long or a tug of 2 ft. 0 in. to 2 ft. 6 in.

Great care should be exercised with all oscillating engines in setting out and making the ports, for on their accuracy depends very largely the efficient functioning of the engine.

Cylinder ports should always be set out as drawing, and have *straight* sides so as to obtain a quick and complete opening to steam and exhaust. Steam block ports should be shaped as diagram. Shaded space must be fractionally wider than cylinder port.

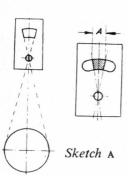

Sketch A

The steam and exhaust ports may well be larger than the cylinder port to allow of greater freedom of ingress and egress to the steam. Left hand sketch shows the area on the port-block swept by the cylinder port which itself will be one-third of this, the middle " third." Any increase in area of the port block ports must naturally be on their *outward* edges.

Fig. 4 is a general arrangement drawing of a simple twin cylinder double acting oscillating engine of the diagonal type for driving a paddle steamer. As the normal speed of paddles is far too low for engine efficiency, reduction gearing is introduced to allow of high rotative engine speed.

Cylinder details are exactly as Fig. 3 and both cylinders drive one crank.

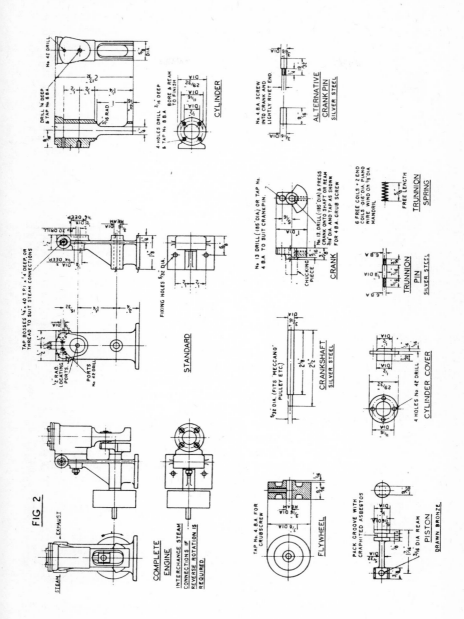

FIG. 2A

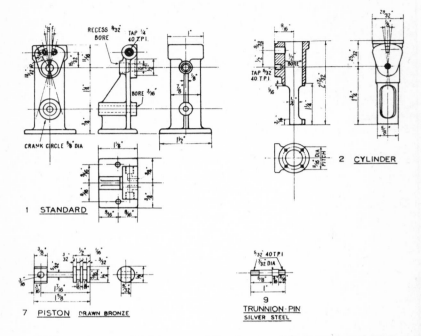

This engine would drive a paddle steamer 5 ft. 0 in. to 6 ft. 0 in. in length, as these boats are almost universally of light type with fine lines. The exceptions are paddle tugs ; for this type the engine would suit a boat up to say 3 ft. 0 in. long.

Just one more point on design and construction, the pivot pin. This unobtrusive item is much more important than at first sight it might be thought to be.

It is the most highly stressed item in the engine, and on its accuracy and good fitting depends to a very large extent the satisfactory functioning and life of the engine.

Fig. 5 shows enlarged detail of a pivot pin and may be taken as a guide.

The enlarged portion should be a good, but free fit in the port block, and as already stated the hole in the port block must be truly at right angles to the port face.

The pin itself must also be truly at right angles to the cylinder port face which in turn must be parallel with the axis of the cylinder.

As a guide to the diameter of the large portion of the pivot pin this may be taken as one-third cylinder bore; where a long stroke

FIG. 3.

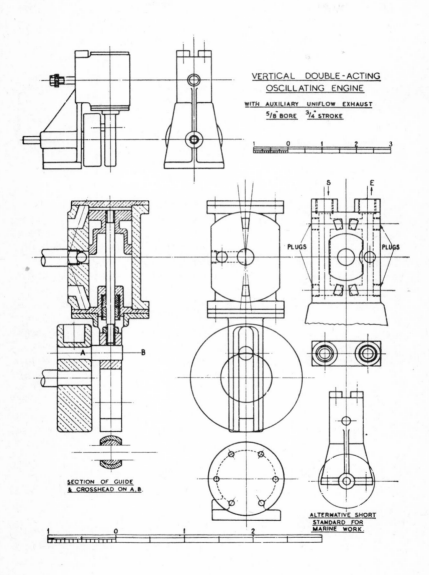

VERTICAL   DOUBLE - ACTING
OSCILLATING ENGINE

WITH AUXILIARY UNIFLOW EXHAUST
$5/8$" BORE $3/4$" STROKE

PLUGS   PLUGS

SECTION OF GUIDE
& CROSSHEAD ON A.B.

ALTERNATIVE SHORT
STANDARD FOR
MARINE WORK.

FIG. 4.

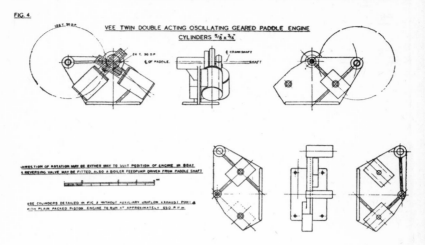

VEE TWIN DOUBLE ACTING OSCILLATING GEARED PADDLE ENGINE
CYLINDERS 5/8 x 3/4"

engine is concerned, say a stroke more than $1\frac{1}{2}$ times bore, this proportion should be increased to two-fifths cylinder bore. These figures give sizes greatly in excess of those usually found in this type of engine, but they are to be thoroughly recommended on the grounds of long wear-free life and sound working.

The use of floating washers to locate the spring is to be strongly recommended together with locknuts to keep the spring adjustment from tending either to tighten itself or to slack off. The spring should be only sufficiently tightened to prevent leakage; anything more wastes power in friction. Of course, the higher the pressure, the tighter the spring will have to be. Oscillating engines of this simple type are not suitable for steam pressures in excess of 40 lb.

FIG. 5.

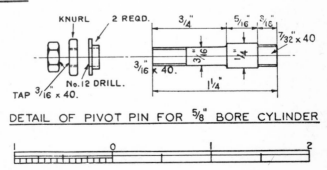

DETAIL OF PIVOT PIN FOR 5/8" BORE CYLINDER

FIG 6

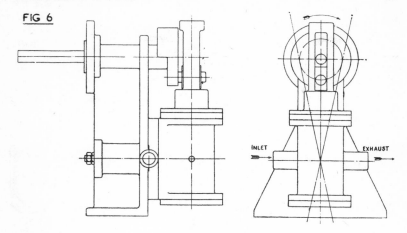

COMPRESSED AIR MOTOR

per sq. in. and 30 lb. is a more usual figure.   A small degree of superheat to the steam is a great advantage.

For the intelligent reader, enough has, I think, been said, clearly to indicate that there are great possibilities for the simple oscillating engine, where cheapness and trouble free reliability over long periods are essential, it is a splendid little power unit.

Fig. 8 shows a simple reversing valve which is applicable either to a S.A. or D.A. engine.   Where an oscillating engine is applied

FIG. 7

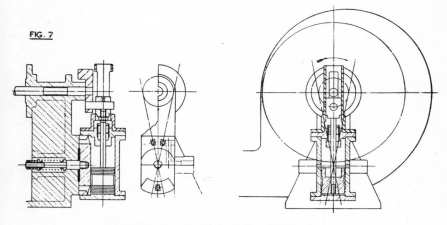

COMPRESSED AIR MOTOR TO DRIVE FAN

FIG. 8

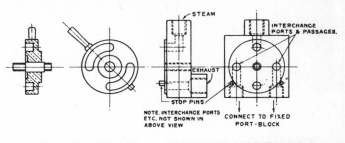

REVERSING VALVE & PIVOT PIN   FIXED PORTION OF REVERSING UNIT

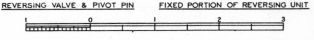

to a crane, a locomotive, or a road vehicle, such a reversing valve is desirable, in its central position it acts as a stop valve, but a main stop valve in the steam line should also be fitted for regulating purposes.

The drawings, Figs. 6 and 7, illustrate a small oscillating engine I made some time ago to work on compressed air and drive a fan.

It embodies all the principles laid down in the foregoing notes. It has a set of " Uniflow " auxiliary exhaust ports; if used with steam these should be rearranged after the style of those in the two D.A. designs, otherwise you will have water and oil slung all over the vicinity.

*Plate 1. Single-acting oscil-
lating engine designed and
built by the late Harry Wedge*

*Plate 2. Single-acting oscillating engine with auxiliary ' uniflow '
exhaust port, trunk guide, combined flywheel and crank disc and
combined stop valve and displacement lubricator. Made by the
author*

CHAPTER 3

SIMPLE FIXED CYLINDER ENGINES

SOME PURIST will say, " Why not slide valve engines ? " The answer is that they are not necessarily slide valve engines, they may be semi-rotary valve engines or poppet valve engines.

Fig. 9 shows a beam engine of very simple type of which a photograph also appears, which I made some years ago. It has several features which should appeal to the model engineer, it has no split bearings at all, it has only one gland and the valve is directly driven from the eccentric without the intervention of bell cranks and links. The whole job was, in my case, built up from odds and ends, the only casting used was for the flywheel.

The valve is a semi-rotary one, and requires no steam chest, its similarity to the principle of the double acting oscillating cylinder will immediately be apparent, but it has the great advantage that, being driven by a separate and adjustable eccentric, it can be made to cut off steam before the end of the stroke and to give an earlier exhaust. This engine too has an auxiliary uniflow exhaust, though in this case owing to the slow speed at which beam engines run (or *should* run) it is a moot point as to whether this offers any advantages. Beam engines were the earliest practical form of rotative steam engine and they have a great fascination. In connection with the parallel motion, great care is necessary to ensure accuracy in the centre distances of the various links, and it is advisable to make some sort of simple drilling or pin jig to ensure this.

As shown, such a semi-rotary-valve is suitable not only for driving by a single eccentric, but for driving by any normal reversing gear such as Stephenson link motion, Walschaerts, Joy, etc. Fig. 10 shows details of the valve and of the port face.

A type of valve in common use in the cheaper type of commercial model " fixed cylinder " engine is the one shown herewith, where no steam-chest or gland is involved and the valve itself is held in place by a spring applied to its back, as shown in the sketch A. The valve here is a " simple " one, i.e. it has no " lap " and thus admits steam for the full length of the stroke and does not open to exhaust until the end of the stroke either. The ports S.S. are the connections to the cylinder ends, just as found on a normal D.A. oscillating or

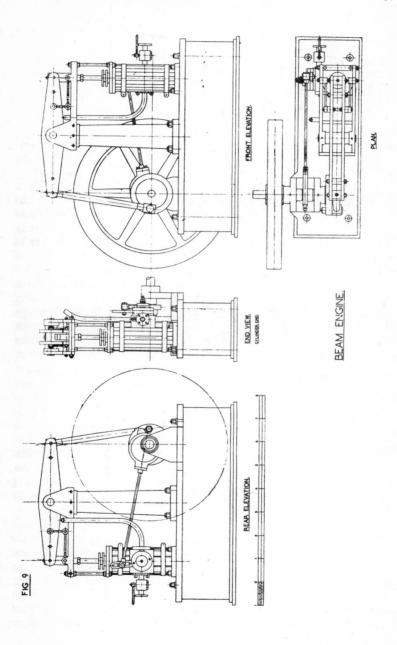

FIG 9

FRONT ELEVATION.

PLAN.

END VIEW.
CYLINDER END.

REAR ELEVATION.

BEAM ENGINE.

Plate 3. Simple beam engine with oscillating valve; flywheel is the only casting used. Built by the author

slide valve cylinder.   The ports P and P1 are steam inlet and exhaust ports, and either port may be used for either purpose.   If P is used for steam inlet then the engine will run in one direction, whereas if P1 is used for steam inlet, then it will run the opposite way, thus by use of a reversing valve as detailed in the chapter on oscillating engines, the engine may be reversed.   This, however, is only possible with the simple lapless valve driven by an eccentric

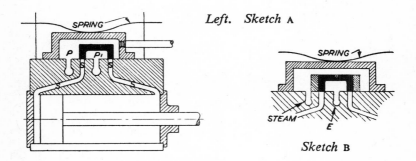

Left.   Sketch A

Sketch B

90 deg. out of phase with the crank.   The principle finds commercial full size application in such engines as ships' steering engines, almost always using a *piston* valve.   It is wasteful of steam but in the case quoted this is of little moment (as the engine runs only very intermittently) as compared with its extreme simplicity and reliability.

There is no point in using such a valve which gives any *working* advantage over the simple oscillating engine, in fact the latter is preferable as being so much simpler.

Such a valve, however, can be made to give early cut-off and release, just as can the normal slide valve, but at the expense of sacrificing the possibility of reversing with a valve.

Sketch B shows a valve of this type, and it should be pointed out that, assuming identical port and port face sizes, this valve will not only require an eccentric of greater throw, but also the eccentric will have to be " advanced," i.e., turned round the shaft to an angle considerably in excess of the 90 deg. which is correct for the simple lapless valve.   " Lap " of valve is double hatched in sketch.

Fig. 11 shows a very simple horizontal engine embodying such a valve and it is an excellent model for a beginner, and, in fact, perhaps a somewhat simpler job than the beam engine.   It can quite well be constructed without the use of any castings at all, other than one for the flywheel.   The guide used for the piston rod is of the

FIG. 10

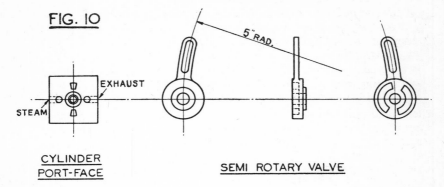

CYLINDER
PORT-FACE

SEMI ROTARY VALVE

VALVE DETAILS FOR 'K' SERIES 4 BEAM ENGINE

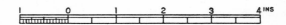

simplest possible type, but is perfectly satisfactory for a model of this nature.

It too, has been largely used for commercial models, particularly the Continental productions, but as designed in this model is considerably more robust.

As in the beam engine there are no split bearings at all. The engine is not intended for continuous hard work, but it will give long and satisfactory service if reasonably treated.

To conclude this chapter I think it would be well to deal as briefly as possible with the principles of the ordinary type of slide valve.

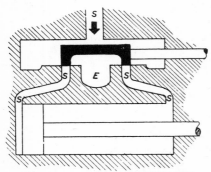

TOTAL TRAVEL OF VALVE 2X WIDTH OF S

Sketch C

The sketch C shows in diagram form a slide valve cylinder with a " simple " slide valve. The piston is shown at one end of the cylinder and the valve in *mid* position.

A moment's consideration will show that the crank must be on its inner dead centre and the eccentric half-way through its travel.

It will also be seen that the valve is in this position

sealing *all* ports, but that the moment it is moved in either direction it will open one port to steam and the other to exhaust.

As shown in the second sketch, D, the eccentric is set to give clockwise rotation to the engine, and thus the valve will move to the *right* letting steam in behind the piston at the left hand end and allowing steam in the right hand portion of the cylinder to escape via the exhaust port E. It will also be appreciated that the left hand port will not be closed again until the engine has made a complete half revolution and the piston has got to the right hand end of the cylinder, similarly the exhaust will not be closed until this position is achieved. Thus we have steam admitted for the full stroke. Finally, the steam in the left hand end will not be released until the end of the stroke either.

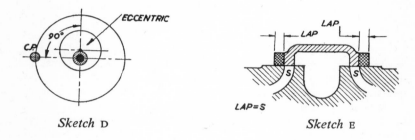

Sketch D   Sketch E

This is a most wasteful arrangement as no use whatever is made of the expansive properties of the steam. Further, in full size practice, the weight of the piston, piston rod crosshead, and connecting rod is considerable and moving forward it gathers great momentum, which under the conditions illustrated has to be absorbed entirely by the crankpin and shaft at the end of each stroke. To overcome this we do two things, one following of necessity on the other. First we add " lap " to the valve. Now, obviously, if we did this to the simple valve, shown in sketch E, and we made the lap as shown equal to the port width the valve would actually never uncover the ports to steam at all, because the eccentric would not move it far enough, so for a start we must increase the travel of our eccentric to twice as much; this will ensure that S-S are fully opened, but if we leave our eccentric set at only 90 deg. in advance of the crank, the opening to steam will not take place until the piston is well down the cylinder, so we have also to " advance " the eccentric by turning it clockwise around the shaft until the relative positions of valve and piston are as shown in sketch F.

This new setting ensures quite a lot of things. (1) Steam will be cut off when the piston has travelled three-quarters of its stroke (strictly this figure is affected by the length of the connecting-rod and is not quite the same for both ends of the cylinder, but for practical purposes the statement may be accepted); (2) the other

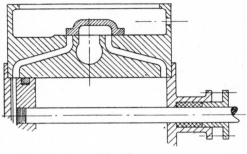

end of the cylinder will be opened to exhaust earlier, thus reducing back pressure; (3) the opening to exhaust will be closed before the piston reaches the end of the cylinder, thus giving a " compression" stage which has two bene-ficial effects, (*a*) it

Sketch F

cushions the inertia and relieves the crankpin, etc., of stress (a matter of little importance in models unless large and high speed ones), (*b*) it raises the temperature of the trapped steam and reduces initial condensation of the incoming steam.

With one or two specialised exceptions slide valves are always made with " outside " or " steam " lap for the reasons outlined above. The exhaust cavity is equally important. Sketches z, z1 and z2 show three variations. z shows the cavity exactly bridging the port bars, this is the form of construction which should

Sketch z   *Sketch* z1   *Sketch* z2

always be used in model work, the fact that it is universal in modern full size loco practice is significant. z1 shows what is known as " exhaust clearance," where the valve cavity over-bridges the port bars. This construction gives earlier release, and actually momentarily puts both ends of the cylinder in communication with one another at every stroke, it is wasteful and has nothing whatever to recommend it, except that it is a help to an engine with inefficient exhaust arrangements. With the valve proportions and eccentric

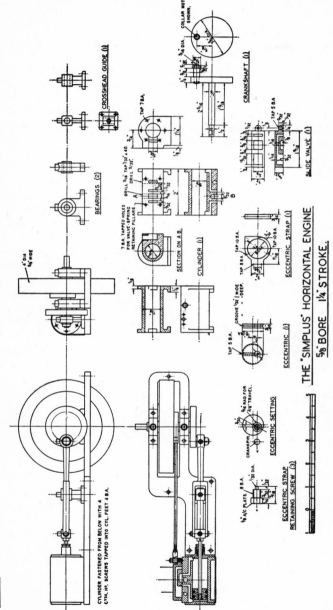

FIG. II.

settings adopted in all the engines described in this book a perfectly
free exhaust will be attained. In effect, they are those adopted by
that master of steam engine valves and valve gears, G. J. Churchward, as the full gear events for his locomotives.

If an engine requires exhaust clearance to make it function
satisfactorily, it is obvious that either its exhaust arrangements,
valve proportions or setting, or valve gear are subject to improvement, maybe all three !

z2 shows " exhaust lap " where the valve cavity does not quite
bridge the port bars. This *retards* point of exhaust release and
raises compression, used in full-size practice where speeds are
high to cushion inertia loads, e.g. marine and rolling mill engines,
but is never needed in models.

The action of the slide valve is not by any means an easy thing
to explain simply; it is, in fact, a complicated and intricate matter,
to which many eminent engineers have had to devote years of
study. I believe it was the great G.W.R. locomotive superintendent, G. J. Churchward, who said that after 20 years close study
of the subject he was just beginning to understand it. To those
who are familiar with Churchward's work, that speaks volumes.

The literature dealing with the slide valve and its working
would fill a good sized library, and it is not a thing that lends itself
to complete simplification for the very obvious reason that in spite
of its inherent constructional simplicity, its working and effects
due to its complex job, are very involved indeed.

I cannot do better than recommend the interested and intelligent
reader who wants really to study its working to get hold of a good
text book on the subject. In spite of all the sneers at text books
they are amongst the greatest possible helps to the intelligent man,
be he a qualified engineer or an amateur enthusiast.

CHAPTER 4

A SIMPLE VERTICAL ENGINE

THE ENGINE illustrated in Fig. 12 is just about as simple an example of an orthodox type of slide valve engine as can be made. It uses a minimum of castings and could, in fact, be made without any at all, though it would save time and trouble at least to have the cylinder and bed made as castings. This design, in common with all the other designs appearing, has ample bearing and wearing surfaces throughout, a most important point if long and wear-free life under hard working conditions is wanted. Whilst it is true that with a decently designed model, the actual bearing loadings are less than those in the full sized job, it is also true that all too frequently lubrication in the model is somewhat haphazard and dust and grit are not so carefully excluded.

As with the beam engine design, solid bush bearings are adopted where possible.

The engine can be run at quite high speeds, 1,000-1,500 r.p.m. continuously without any ill effects or undue wear, and is suitable either for marine or stationary work; for the former a much smaller flywheel is used than for the latter. The crankshaft is balanced and may be made from the solid, from a forging or by one of the several different methods of building up. The crosshead and its guide are of a type unusual in model work but used extensively in some very fine small launch engines in past years, before the petrol motor supplanted the steam plant.

The connecting-rod is of the standard marine type with a round body and an eye little end, which works on a gudgeon pin fixed in the crosshead; both eye and pin should be thoroughly case-hardened, and the pin should be a really good running fit in the eye. Incidentally, the big end is the only split bearing on the engine. The cylinder has a built-on-port face which enables proper full sized passages to be arranged between port and cylinder barrel.

To get efficient results one *must* provide ports of adequate size, and passages of at least equivalent cross section. That has been established and proved efficient practice amongst steam engineers for over 150 years, and it is highly improbable at this late date,

FIG. 12.

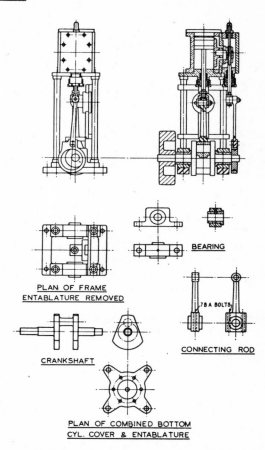

BEARING

PLAN OF FRAME
ENTABLATURE REMOVED

7 B A BOLTS

CRANKSHAFT

CONNECTING ROD

PLAN OF COMBINED BOTTOM
CYL. COVER & ENTABLATURE

SIMPLE VERTICAL SLIDE VALVE MARINE ENGINE
$^5/_8$" BORE $^5/_8$" STROKE

that anyone is likely to be able to contribute anything new and of any real importance to our knowledge of these matters.

The base of frame is of unusual but sound mechanical design, it is made as it is to suit the solid bushed main bearings, whilst allowing the crankshaft to be inserted or removed.

Plate 4. *Stuart No. 1 rebuilt by the author and fitted with balanced crank, reversing gear, stop valve and displacement lubricator*

The eccentric is a plain flanged disc, with a cover plate to retain the strap in place; it is located on the shaft by means of a grub-screw.

The grubscrew should have a *flat* end, not pointed, and the bore of the eccentric should be a good push fit on the shaft, on no account must there be any play here, else the eccentric will never " stay put."

A hole is bored in the strap to allow of a screwdriver being inserted to operate the grubscrew for adjusting purposes. A diagram, Fig. 13, shows the recommended valve and eccentric setting. It will be noted that the valve can be adjusted without having to turn the valve spindle. The upper end of the valve rod works in a dummy gland and the lower end through a long stuffing box and gland so that there is no need for any additional guide.

The bottom cylinder cover also serves as the entablature of the frame structure. Care must be exercised to get all the columns exactly the same length over their shoulders otherwise the cylinder will stand cock-eyed to the bed and your whole alignment will be upset.

Here it might be well to stress the whole question of accurate alignment, a matter too often passed lightly over or completely ignored; too much trouble cannot be taken to ensure such things as cylinder axis projected passing through centre of crankshaft, cylinder axis and crankshaft axis being truly at right angles, cross-head slide being truly aligned in both planes with cylinder axis, port face and valve rod being linable with cylinder axis and the valve rod axis when projected passing through crankshaft axis (when valve is direct driven, as in the present case, of course). All these things must be observed if you are to have a mechanically efficient, free-running, and wear-free engine. Trouble taken to attain the greatest possible accuracy here will be amply rewarded. It might be well to mention here that the general subject of lubrication is dealt with separately later on.

A suitable boiler pressure would be between 60 and 80 lb. per sq. inch. So far as strength is concerned the engine would be perfectly satisfactory at 150 lb. per sq. inch, but unless the valve and valve gear were modified to give an earlier cut off, it would be somewhat wasteful of steam at this higher pressure.

If the cylinder is made of a good quality gunmetal a reasonably high superheat will give considerably increased efficiency and decreased steam and fuel consumption.

This engine is suitable, if used for marine work for a boat of from 2 ft. 6 in. to 4 ft. 6 in. depending on the lines and weight. It is in no sense a racing engine, but it is capable of putting up quite a good performance and of keeping it up more or less indefinitely so long as it is kept well and suitably lubricated.

FIG. 13.

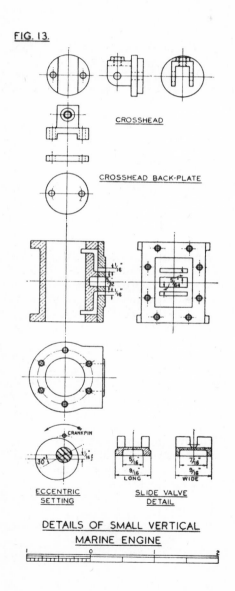

CROSSHEAD

CROSSHEAD BACK-PLATE

ECCENTRIC
SETTING

SLIDE VALVE
DETAIL

DETAILS OF SMALL VERTICAL
MARINE ENGINE

CHAPTER 5

COMPOUND ENGINES

TO GO fully into the principles of compounding or multi-stage expansion is quite beyond the scope of this little book; it is a vast subject in itself and only the barest outline of the principles involved will be attempted.

It will be remembered from Chapter 1 that as soon as the steam begins to expand in a cylinder its temperature begins to fall; this means that as the piston reaches the end of its stroke the steam is at a much lower temperature than it was at the commencement, and this in turn means that that end of the cylinder and the piston itself are in consequence cooled down. Immediately steam is admitted to this end of the cylinder it has to warm up the piston and cylinder walls, and to do so some of it must condense and is in consequence wasted.

Now it will, I am sure, not be a strain upon the intelligence of the average reader to deduce from this that the less the difference in temperature between the entering steam and exhaust steam in any one cylinder the less the condensation losses. On the other hand, if we use high pressure steam and use it expansively there must be a wide difference between its initial and final temperatures. These facts being realised, it is fairly obvious that if we spread this expansion process over two or more cylinders, the individual variations in temperature and consequential condensation losses will be correspondingly reduced. It will also be fairly obvious, that the steam having already expanded in one cylinder, will require more elbow room in the second cylinder, hence each succeeding cylinder is made larger in diameter than the preceding one. (I am ignoring special cases, which are rare, where the extra capacity of the cylinder is gained by increased stroke, though in locomotive work it is not unusual to find both bore and stroke increased in the l.p. cylinders, this is due to constructional limitations.)

I do not propose to go into the question of cylinder ratios or of valve settings, it would be outside our immediate scope, but the reader who wishes seriously to study this matter will find ample information in steam engine text books.

For the maximum information in the minimum of space the

matter to be found on this subject in *The Mechanical World* year book in the first 10 years of this century is unbeatable, and is to be most thoroughly recommended.

For model work there is no point whatever in making a compound engine of the non-condensing variety to work at less than 110 to 120 lb. per sq. in. pressure; below that a " simple " will almost always give more economical results. Condensing too, is beyond the scope of this book, not because it is not of first rate importance; it is, but because it is such a very large and involved subject bringing in its train a whole lot of ancillary apparatus such as the condenser itself, air pumps, circulating pumps, etc. [*In this new edition Condensing and the apparatus required is fairly comprehensively covered in Chapter* 14.]

Fig. 14 shows a pair of compound cylinders to replace the twin H.P. cylinders of the model shown in Fig. 22, whilst Fig. 15 details of the valves and eccentric settings. Given good workmanship, such an engine working at 120 lb. sq. in. pressure might be expected to show some economy in steam consumption per b.h.p. as compared with that of the twin cylinder version. It should be appreciated that the actual power output of the compound, working at the same speed as the twin, will be appreciably less; this will be obvious when we consider that the compound has one cylinder taking boiler steam $1\frac{3}{8}$ in. bore by $\frac{7}{8}$ in. stroke, whereas the twin has two cylinders, $1\frac{3}{16}$ in. bore by $\frac{7}{8}$ in. stroke both taking boiler steam though at a somewhat lower pressure. The compound (or triple or quadruple expansion) is a most fascinating model and provides opportunity for much interesting experiment and study; when it comes to producing the simplest type of power unit, however, I should always plump for a single or twin cylinder job, the latter only if a self-starting engine was required. Even for small power production say, for a steam launch engine, I should not use a compound under at least 10 h.p. not because it would not be possible to gain *any* economy thereby, it undoubtedly would, but because, in my view, this thermal economy would be quite outweighed by the amount of extra work and complication involved in the design and building of a compound. Of course, if the launch were to be used in salt water, then condensing and compounding become essential.

If you are making a really high grade model, say, of a tug or a trawler, by all means build a compound engine for it, and fit it with reverse gear and a condenser, if on the other hand you are building the same type of model as a good hard working proposition, then fit a twin cylinder non-condensing engine without reversing gear.

Apart from locomotives, traction engines, and one or two special varieties of other engines which are rarely modelled anyhow,

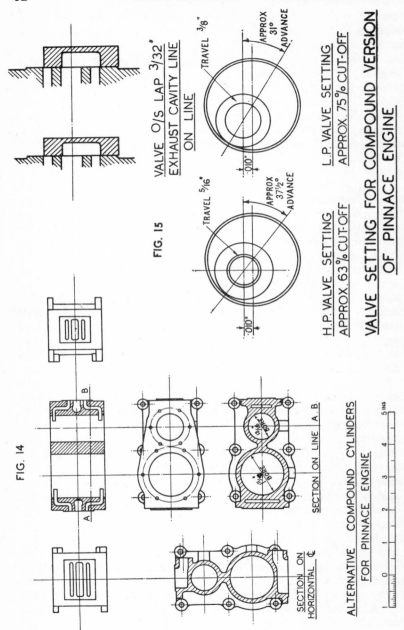

VALVE O/S LAP 3/32"
EXHAUST CAVITY LINE
ON LINE

FIG. 15

TRAVEL 3/8"

APPROX 31° ADVANCE

L.P. VALVE SETTING
APPROX. 75% CUT-OFF

TRAVEL 5/16"

APPROX 37½° ADVANCE

H.P. VALVE SETTING
APPROX. 63% CUT-OFF

VALVE SETTING FOR COMPOUND VERSION
OF PINNACE ENGINE

FIG. 14

SECTION ON LINE A. B.

SECTION ON HORIZONTAL ₵

ALTERNATIVE COMPOUND CYLINDERS
FOR PINNACE ENGINE

reversing gear is of no real use in model work, though it is admittedly fascinating to operate and watch; obviously it is a matter on which each individual will make a decision in accordance with his own ideas; up to now in spite of so many encroachments upon our individual freedom of action, in such a matter at least we can still please ourselves. In model work most people will settle the size of the H.P. cylinder first and proceed to make the L.P. of a size to suit; this is an exact inversion of the correct procedure wherein the size of the L.P. cylinder is first decided on the assumption that *all* the power of the engine is produced therein. Having settled this point the correct dimensions of a suitable H.P. cylinder can be calculated.

Compound engines are found in both vertical and horizontal forms, and in addition as side by side diagonal or " Vee " diagonal for paddle boat work. The " Vee " diagonal form has been used too for launch engines (screw propeller) and for steam lorries and cars. Where the " Vee " form is used it is usual to find both sets of motion driving one crankpin.

Generally, for working model steam engines, I do not favour the use of piston valves; in spite of everything said by some professional model engineers, it remains a fact that many people find them very difficult to make steam-tight in the first place, and even more difficult to keep steam-tight, and amongst these people I have met some highly skilled craftsmen too. The argument that everything is easy once you know how is in my opinion both dangerous and misleading. Very few worth-while things in this world are easy. It is just by facing and overcoming difficulties that mankind has risen from the primeval slime, and it is in the overcoming of the manifold difficulties of model engineering that lies its supreme fascination.

If there were any truth in the preposterous statement that "everything is easy when you know how," anyone could, by reading the instructions in a good book on rifle shooting become a Bisley prizewinner with no trouble at all. I am a fairly good shot and have done quite a little musketry instruction, and I have yet to find the man who, after the most thorough course of *instruction*, can lie down and make a " possible " first time, few will reach 80 per cent., many less than 50 per cent., and a few will not even hit the target at all.

A valve slide, or piston, which is for all practical purposes dead steam-tight when stationary, is far from it when moving and will be found if properly tested to be leaking anything up to 20 per cent. of the total steam consumption of the engine. The piston valve offering a larger leakage area than an equivalent slide-valve is the worse culprit in this respect. The test so beloved by the self-styled practical man of setting the piston valve in its mid-position, opening the cylinder drain cocks, and observing the lack of leakage through them has little practical value for the obvious reason that the valve is *not* stationary when working. Further, the slide valve is self-compensating for wear, whilst the solid piston valve, used of necessity in small sizes, very obviously is *not*.

Anyhow, I do *not* recommend the use of piston valves generally in model work, but in a compound there is something less to be said against their use for the H.P. cylinder only on the score of leakage, as this is not wasted, but serves to put up the m.e.p. in the L.P. steam chest ; further, on the positive side with H.P. steam a piston valve properly made absorbs a lot less power in friction than does a slide valve.

Where a piston valve is used, it should have " inside admission " as this relieves the valve spindle gland of everything but exhaust pressure.

Actually the use of a piston valve for the H.P. cylinder and flat slide valve for the L.P. cylinder is common practice in full sized work.

The advantages of using superheated steam are very great with model compound engines, and if any reader wants to try an interesting experiment I suggest he should get hold of a decent small compound model and remove the receiver pipe from H.P. exhaust to L.P. steam and replace it by a coiled pipe, placed in a vertical insulated case and apply a bunsen gas (or other convenient) flame to it whilst the engine is running.   I think he will be surprised at the result.

CHAPTER 6

A HORIZONTAL MILL ENGINE

THE ENGINE illustrated in Fig. 16 is of a type which in the latter half of the nineteenth century and during the first decade of the twentieth, was to be found in factories and workshops all over the world. The model represents to a scale of 1 in. to 1 ft. one of the smaller and simpler types, actually an engine of 9 in. bore by 18 in. stroke.

Again the design has been worked out so as to keep the number of castings used to a minimum. In actual practice engines of this type were very frequently installed so that the outboard bearing was housed in a wall-box built into the engine-house wall with the flywheel and pulley mounted between it and the main bearing. Incidentally, though a perfectly satisfactory method, this was a beastly arrangement for the maintenance fitter who had the thankless task of adjusting the outboard bearing; unless there was access from the *outside* of the wall, adjustment of this bearing usually involved removing the crankshaft complete with flywheel and pulley, and as often as not it was very awkward to rig up lifting tackle. In the case of our model we use an outboard bearing exactly the same as the main bearing but $\frac{1}{16}$ in. less bore mounted on the metal baseplate so that the model is a unit.

Again, by using a crankpin, with a detachable retaining-collar and an eccentric strap of special construction, split bearings are entirely avoided. Here it might be well to point out that if bearings are designed with ample area, properly made, and good quality materials used and finally, if they are kept clean and well lubricated, their wear-free life will be almost indefinite, the alleged advantages of " split bearings adjustable for wear " are largely illusory, and are certainly outweighed by the great gain in simplicity of construction obtained by using the bush type of bearing. I have used bush bearings in small power engines up to 10 or 12 h.p. with great success over long periods of really hard work.

The crosshead and slide bars are of an old-fashioned but very sound and simple type, and provided care is taken in the first place to ensure that the wrist-pin or gudgeon pin is truly at right angles to the piston, you will be assured of a free running engine for both the connecting-rod and guide slippers float.

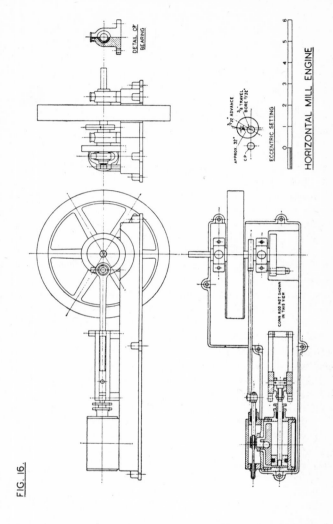

FIG. 16.

The guide bars should be of silver steel, which can be obtained in square section, the crosshead should be cut out of a piece of mild steel whilst the gudgeon pin should be case-hardened mild steel, a driving fit in the crosshead. The slide blocks may be gunmetal cast-iron, or mild steel—if the latter, case-hardened.

The connecting-rod should be of mild-steel and its eye should be a really good fit on the wrist pin and should also be case-hardened.

The flywheel, one of the few castings, is 6 in. diameter, but this size is not critical, it may be as large as 8 in. diameter or as small as 4½ in. in the former case it may have a lighter rim, in the latter it should have a heavier one.

The crankshaft and crank disc can be turned from the solid or the disc can be made separately. If the latter course is followed it may be fixed to the shaft either by force fitting or brazing. If you have tools for accurately measuring both the hole in the disc, and the shaft, and you are sufficiently skilful to be able to turn your shaft accurately to 0·0005 in. larger than the hole, then I recommend a force fit job, if not a brazed job.

In the former case fit a key as in the sketch, just a plain driving fit filed off flush. On no account try to make a force fit and then braze it " just in case." If you do this you have wasted your force fit, for the heat necessary to braze will release all the stress of the forced fit. If you make a force fit job and it takes, say, 400 lb. to force it home, after which you heat the whole job up to redness, let it cool and force it apart again; you will find it will probably not require more than 100 lb. to force it out again, probably, in fact, much less.

If you are not confident about your ability to make a good force fit, do not try, or if you do, try it on something that does not matter first. It is well to leave a little metal on the disc to machine off after assembly on the shaft, holding the latter in a true running collet; this will ensure your disc running absolutely true. Nothing looks worse than a crank of this type with a wobble on it; however slight it will be noticeable.

Of course, the hole for the crankpin should be drilled in the disc before assembly if the disc is made separately. Be sure the hole is accurately located and truly at right angles to the face of the disc.

The crankpin should be a light driving fit in the disc and secured in place with a fine thread nut, 40 t.p.i. is ideal for this purpose, or alternatively, riveted.

Obviously the threaded portion of the pin should stand under the back face of the disc, otherwise you will not be able properly to tighten up the retaining nut.

Be sure that the bores of your eccentric, pulley, and flywheel are all a good push fit on your shaft otherwise they won't run true, and in the case of the eccentric it will be apt to shift on the shaft both radially and sideways. Fit little oilcups to the main and outboard bearings and to the big end of the connecting-rod, and see that they are kept full when running the engine.

As laid out the valve and valve gear will give a cut-off of 75 per cent., and a full opening of the ports to steam and exhaust. This

Plate 5. Model Horizontal engine with Joy reversing gear and shaft throttle governor, made by the author

Plate 6. Close up view of Plate 5 showing reversing gear, throttle valve and governor

type of engine was a comparatively slow speed job running usually at 120-150 r.p.m., and it will look much nicer running if the speed is kept down to not more than 250 r.p.m., than if it is allowed to run so fast that " the motion is a blur " which, in the eyes of some people seems to be the apogee of model performance !

An engine of this type always had some form of governor, but in the first place, this may be omitted on the model; in a later chapter I will be dealing with the general principles of governors, and the builder can later fit whatever type he fancies. I suggest a simple form of displacement lubricator for the cylinder.

CHAPTER 7

A SINGLE CYLINDER TWIN SCREW ENGINE

THE LITTLE engine described and illustrated (Fig. 17) is not novel in principle. In fact, it must be 50 years old. Nevertheless, it is a type which does not seem to be at all well known, and it is one which has, where twin screws are required, many advantages. Nearly all twin screw arrangements, other than those embodying separate engines, utilise more or less complicated systems of gearing, which in smaller sizes particularly, waste a lot of power. This engine, too, uses gearing, but in this case its function is merely to ensure synchronisation of the two sides and it has no power-transmitting function whatever.

By the method of construction adopted the gears become the crank-webs and the whole issue is totally enclosed in an oiltight case. The engine would work without the gears, but in such a case it would be *possible* for both shafts to turn in the *same* direction.

The engine is extremely simple in its essentials and is made entirely without castings. It is of such a size as to be capable of driving a fine lined boat of 4 ft. 6 in. to 5 ft. 6 in. long at a reasonable speed. The engine is in no sense intended as a racing job, though capable of putting up a good performance. The aim has been to produce a simple and compact twin screw engine which will give a good cylinder performance and, for its size, a reasonable thermal efficiency.

The balance is quite good and the arrangement of the connecting-rods and crosshead is such that the necessity for guiding the piston rod is little more than nominal.

The ports and passages are large and the valve travel long, the cut-off being of the order of 72 per cent. with a full opening to exhaust.

The passages are milled out and the port face made separately and silver-soldered into position. This gives clean full size smooth sided ports and passages and enables sharp corners to be eliminated. There are no split bearings at all (unless some purist wants so to call the valve eccentric strap). The wrist pins and connecting-rod

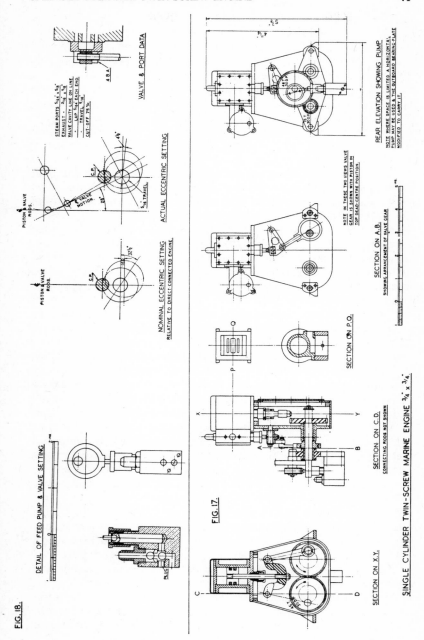

FIG. 18.

DETAIL OF FEED PUMP & VALVE SETTING

VALVE & PORT DATA

STEAM PORTS ⁵⁄₆₄ x ⁵⁄₈"
EXHAUST - ³⁄₁₆ x ⁵⁄₈"
VALVE CAVITY. LINE ON LINE
LAP ⁵⁄₆₄ EACH END
TRAVEL ⁵⁄₁₆
CUT-OFF 75%

4 B.A.

ACTUAL ECCENTRIC SETTING

C.P.
PISTON & VALVE RODS.
VALVE MOTION.
⁵⁄₁₆ TRAVEL.
28°

NOMINAL ECCENTRIC SETTING
RELATIVE TO DIRECT CONNECTED ENGINE

C.P.
PISTON & VALVE RODS.
32½°

REAR ELEVATION SHOWING PUMP

NOTE WHERE SPACE IS LIMITED A HORIZONTAL
PUMP MAY BE USED & THE OUTBOARD BEARING PLATE
MODIFIED TO CARRY IT.

NOTE IN THESE TWO VIEWS VALVE
GEAR IS SHOWN WITH PISTON IN
TOP DEAD-CENTRE POSITION

SECTION ON A.B.

SHOWING ARRANGEMENT OF VALVE GEAR

SECTION ON P.Q.

SECTION ON C.D.
CONNECTING RODS NOT SHOWN

FIG. 17.

SECTION ON X.Y.

SINGLE CYLINDER TWIN-SCREW MARINE ENGINE ³⁄₄" x ³⁄₄".

eye ends are case-hardened, as are also the crankpins; the connecting-rod big ends are bronze bushed.

A self-contained feed pump, geared down 15 to 46 is incorporated and this delivers through an exhaust feedwater heater which will effect quite a considerable thermal economy.

Cylinder lubrication is by a large displacement lubricator, with splash lubrication to crank chamber, and oil cups to main bearings and eccentric. The latter is of comparatively large size as too are the joint pins and pivot of the rocking arm, for the valve is large and with high pressure steam and the engine running at high speed, heavy loadings are imposed upon the valve gear.

The cylinder body is lagged with flannel or felt with a light sheet-metal casing whilst the top cover too is lagged and covered with a spun metal cap. Needle drain valves are fitted top and bottom of the cylinder and to the steam-chest.

Piston is packed with two rings of $\frac{1}{8}$ in. square, braided graphited asbestos, made with scarfed joints just like a metal piston ring. As shown on the drawing, the driving ends of the shafts are fitted with two-pin drivers, but any other form of driving coupling can be fitted as conditions may require.

The angular setting of the eccentric rod and the splayed rocker are adopted so as to give reasonable length to both and thus to reduce angularity, they have, of course, no influence whatever on the normal motion of the valve.

Large bearing surfaces are provided throughout and if the engine is made with good materials and workmanship, and properly lubricated with suitable lubricant, it will have a very long life indeed before appreciable wear will appear. It is intended to be worked with a moderate degree of superheat; if it is wished to get a higher efficiency there is no reason why a cast-iron cylinder, piston, and slide valve should not be used; with a higher pressure (the intended pressure for this engine is up to 100 lb., but the bearings will comfortably stand 150 lb.) and superheat. In such case it would be well to provide for mechanically lubricating the cylinder and valve. Under favourable conditions this little engine could comfortably give out $\frac{1}{4}$ b.h.p. at 2,500 r.p.m. I do not propose to deal with the actual making of the engine which is a perfectly straightforward job for any amateur mechanic of reasonable skill and experience, but there are a few constructional points worth mentioning.

Particular care should be exercised in setting out the holes for the crankpins.

If you look at diagram *A* you will see that if say the l.h. crankpin falls on a radial line cutting through the centre of a tooth the r.h. crankpin must locate on a radial line cutting through the centre

Plate 7. Horizontal engine with flywheel governor giving variable cut-off. Cylinder and trunk guides are the only castings. Made by the author

(Below) The original bed, background, and the new bed, foreground; new bed is entirely fabricated

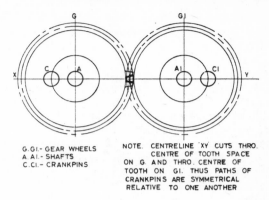

G.GI.- GEAR WHEELS
A.AI.- SHAFTS
C.CI.- CRANKPINS

NOTE. CENTRELINE 'XY' CUTS THRO.
CENTRE OF TOOTH SPACE
ON G. AND THRO. CENTRE OF
TOOTH ON GI. THUS PATHS OF
CRANKPINS ARE SYMMETRICAL
RELATIVE TO ONE ANOTHER

of a tooth-space. This, of course, is very obvious once attention is called thereto, but just the same an easy one to miss, and unless it is right the engine will not work.

The piston should be a real good fit in the cylinder bore, *without its packing* clearance of the order of 0·0005 in. (half a thou.); this will make a lot of difference to the steam consumption.

It should be finish turned on its own rod to ensure concentricity; if you lap it to final size use a soft lap and a soft abrasive.

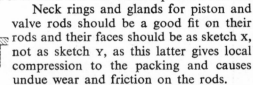

Neck rings and glands for piston and valve rods should be a good fit on their rods and their faces should be as sketch x, not as sketch y, as this latter gives local compression to the packing and causes undue wear and friction on the rods.

Sketch x   If properly packed, glands do not   *Sketch* y
need to be very tight, only just sufficiently
so to prevent leakage. Always take up a gland which shows any sign of leakage. If you cannot stop the leakage without undue tightening, strip out the old packing and re-pack. For small glands you cannot beat stranded " Palmetto " a graphited asbestos product.

One more point, take great care that the spacing of the main bearing holes is accurate. If it is slack you will have backlash in your gears and if it is tight they either will not mesh or will create much friction.

The positioning of the feet which carry the engine may be varied to suit conditions; that is one of the great advantages of built-up construction.

The eccentric should be a really good stiff push fit on the shaft, an eccentric that is loose in the bore is almost impossible to keep properly set permanently under hard working conditions.

For those who want the simplest possible job both feed pump and feedwater heater may be omitted, which will save quite a bit of work.

Regarding a suitable size and type of boiler this will depend greatly on the conditions that the engine is required to fulfil. For medium performance a boiler of the centre-flue cross tube type disposing 100 sq. in. of heating surface or thereabouts and working at 70-80 lb. per sq. in., would suit admirably.

For high performance a " Scott " or " Yarrow " type watertube boiler disposing say, 150 sq. in. heating surface and working at 100-120 lb. per sq. in., would fill the bill, whilst for maximum performance a similar type of boiler disposing say, 200 sq. in. of heating surface and working at 150 lb. per sq. in. would be about right.

In all cases it is assumed that firing arrangements are satisfactory, petrol or paraffin in the blowlamp type of burner suits the centre flue and Scott type of boiler and a silent type of petrol or paraffin burner is admirable for the Yarrow. Other types of boiler may suit special cases, such for instance, as the " Stuart " two drum water tube type, modified locomotive type, or, of course, with cast-iron cylinder, etc., the flash or monotube type.

The whole subject of marine boilers is a most complicated one, there is no " best " type for any and every occasion, but there is a very wide choice of good and satisfactory types. Broadly, for average performance the tank types such as the centre flue or Scotch (not " Scott " which is a water-tube type) are best and easiest to handle; for high performance or racing, the water-tube or flash type is almost essential to success.

Your water feed problems are much simpler with the " tank " types, as you have much greater capacity of water compared to evaporation rate than is the case with the water-tube type. Whatever type you use, remember to utilise steampipes of adequate size and any valves on them should have a clear passage at least equal to the cross-sectional area of the pipe, when fully opened. For an engine of the size of the one just dealt with the bore of the pipe should not be less than 7/32 in. and preferably $\frac{1}{4}$ in. Your aim should be to maintain in the steam-chest a pressure very near that in the boiler, even when the engine is flat out.

There are two methods of obtaining power from a small steam engine. The first may fairly be called the popular one of providing a cylinder larger than is really necessary and working it at a low efficiency. This in effect is analogous to the old-fashioned " woolly " low-compression slow-moving petrol engine which older readers will so well remember.

The other is to extract the highest possible cylinder performance from a suitable sized cylinder.

That is the modern and efficient method, and can again be likened to the modern high-compression, high-revving petrol engine.

That is the engineer's way of doing the job, but it does not depend on efficient design and construction of the cylinder valve and valve gear alone; it involves the whole of the apparatus concerned in the steam supply from its inlet inside the boiler to its admission point to the steam-chest. It also involves the whole of the exhaust line, too.

Your cylinder valve and valve gear may be of first-rate design and construction, but unless all the other parts involved in the pressure cycle are equally well designed and constructed you will not reach the efficiency of which your cylinder is capable.

To obtain good and efficient results along these lines you must be familiar with the fundamental laws governing the functioning of the apparatus you propose to design and construct.

Let me close this chapter by a quotation from an editorial in that great British technical journal *The Engineer*.

" It is idle to argue that Engineering is not an exact science, and that therefore a degree of looseness may be permitted, for assuredly it should be the desire of each of us to make it as exact as possible and ever keep abreast of the best modern practice.

" The so-called rule-of-thumb methods of our ancestors are rapidly passing away, and rough and ready thoughts and actions should similarly be buried."

Those words express far more cogently and succinctly than I could possibly do my own firmly held opinions.

CHAPTER 8

ENCLOSED TYPES OF STEAM ENGINE

IN THE model world the great majority of " enclosed " type of engine, by which is meant engines having all or most of their moving parts enclosed in an oil-tight case, are of the twin cylinder single acting type with a single overhead valve serving both cylinders. These are excellently exemplified by the Stuart Turner series ranging from the " Star " to the " Sirius," the latter quite capable of doing continuous useful work.

I believe the Stuart model "BB" which was a single cylinder double acting engine of normal type, is no longer made, which is a pity, as it was a fine little unit for marine work or for driving direct a small dynamo or centrifugal pump.

Fig. 19 shows a simple single cylinder totally enclosed single acting " Uniflow " engine with a poppet valve. A " Uniflow " engine is one in which the steam is exhausted through a port or series of ports in the cylinder wall uncovered by the piston at the outward end of its stroke; it possesses certain theoretical and practical advantages over the more usual type in which the steam, after having done its work, exhausts through the port through which it entered the cylinder. In Chapter 1 the effects of cylinder condensation were explained and it was pointed out that as the steam expanded as the piston moved towards the end of its stroke it lost heat and some of it condensed whilst at the same time this necessarily meant that the piston and cylinder walls were cooled down; this, in turn, entailed some loss of heat of the incoming steam for the return stroke. In the uniflow engine we have still, of course, the same initial condensation and cooling, but the cool steam passes out round the cool portion of the cylinder, and does not have to flow back and cool the *inlet* end and passages. Thus, with the uniflow system we have a more or less permanent temperature gradient in one direction only, and the incoming steam does not have to re-heat partially cooled cylinder walls at every stroke. The economies brought about by this are very real in full size work, and quite appreciable in model work, in addition to which the system does enable us to make quite considerable simplification in design and construction.

47

Plate 8.   Single acting enclosed engine with semi-rotary valve.   Made by the author

The use of a poppet valve has, for this type of engine, much to recommend it, for it is simple to make, easy to keep steam-tight, and eminently suitable for really hot high pressure steam.   The operating cam should be made of mild-steel and thoroughly case-hardened as too should be the intermediate push spindle, its adjustable tappet end and the lower end of the stem of the actual valve. The cam works under excellent conditions as to lubrication and it and the intermediate push spindle should have a long wear-free life.   No packing is used on the valve spindle, but a number of shallow square bottomed grooves, as sketch should be turned in the portion of the valve spindle which works in the guide, see sketch A which acts as

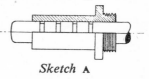

Sketch A

what is known as a labyrinth packing.   The grooves should be about 10 thou. deep and 1/32 in. wide.   The valve spindle should be a really good fit in the guide which should itself be reamed. The spring should be made from piano wire of 22 gauge.

The valve is comparatively small but as the engine is intended to

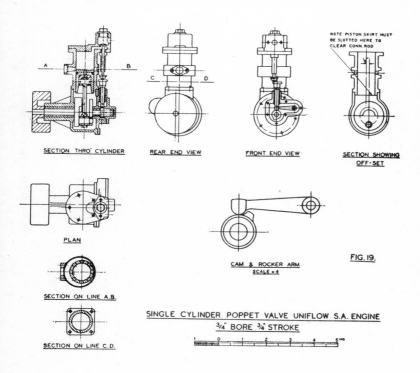

SECTION THRO' CYLINDER   REAR END VIEW   FRONT END VIEW   SECTION SHOWING OFF-SET

PLAN

SECTION ON LINE A.B.

SECTION ON LINE C.D.

CAM & ROCKER ARM
SCALE × 4

FIG. 19.

SINGLE CYLINDER POPPET VALVE UNIFLOW S.A. ENGINE
3/4" BORE 3/4" STROKE

NOTE PISTON SKIRT MUST BE SLOTTED HERE TO CLEAR CONN. ROD

work at high pressure and superheat it will be found to admit ample steam even at the highest speeds. Reverting for a moment to the cam, this should be a really good fit on the crankshaft; if it is not you are very liable to have trouble in keeping it from moving around the shaft when working and so upsetting the timing.

The stresses on it are quite high, so two taper pins are provided to lock it. I have adopted an unusual arrangement of crankshaft (at least it is unusual in steam practice though frequently found in model i.c. engine work, notably in some of Mr. E. T. Westbury's excellent designs). The crankshaft proper is of the overhung single web type, as this is a simpler job to make than the double webbed variety, and properly designed and made, just as sound, mechanically speaking. The outer end of the crankpin drives a follower crank, upon the shaft of which is carried the cam which operates the valve. The connecting-rod is $2\frac{1}{4}$ strokes in length and has very large bearing surfaces for both big and little ends.

The cylinder is arranged on the desaxé principle by which is meant that it is off-set so that its axis is to one side of that of the crankshaft. This is done so that the angularity of the connecting-rod on the downward power stroke is reduced. Of course, it is correspondingly increased on the upward stroke, but on that stroke no work is being done and there is little thrust to be overcome. The principle is in fairly common use in petrol engine practice. Obviously its use is restricted to engines running in one direction only.

The connecting-rod is made from a billet of mild steel, with the big end bushed with gunmetal or phosphor bronze, preferably of the chill cast variety, and the little end thoroughly case-hardened and working on a case-hardened wrist pin.

The piston is a built-up job, the fork which carries the gudgeon or wrist pin is of mild steel and is fixed to the piston head by four countersunk head steel screws.

It is essential that the threads of these screws should be a good fit in their holes, that the countersinks for them should correctly match the angle of the heads, and finally, that they should be screwed up really tight. This form of construction is simple to carry out and it has the great advantage that *should* the wrist pin ever work loose it cannot damage the cylinder walls.

If your skill runs to making piston rings, I strongly recommend fitting one to the piston as shown, preferably made of centrifugally-cast iron, or alternatively, from alloy steel, say, 3 per cent. nickel. This, of course, involves a built-up piston, as it is next to impossible to spring on such tiny rings over a solid piston without either breaking or distorting them. If you don't fancy rings, then you

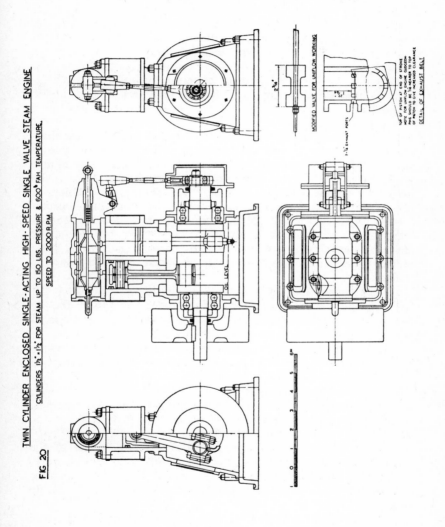

TWIN CYLINDER ENCLOSED SINGLE-ACTING HIGH-SPEED SINGLE VALVE STEAM ENGINE

CYLINDERS 1½" – 1½" FOR STEAM UP TO 150 LBS. PRESSURE & 600° FAH. TEMPERATURE,
SPEED TO 2000 R.P.M.

FIG 20

MODIFIED VALVE FOR UNIFLOW WORKING

TOP OF PISTON AT END OF STROKE
NOTE FOR UNIFLOW ENGINE GUDGEON
PINS SHOULD BE ⅛ NEARER TO TOP
OF PISTON TO GIVE INCREASED CLEARANCE

DETAIL OF EXHAUST BELT

can use the simpler piston with labyrinth grooves, which as well as reducing leakage assist lubrication.

In either case the piston should be a really good fit with a clearance not exceeding 0·0005 in. to 0·00075 in. at the most. The greatest care should be taken over the cylinder bore and piston fit, the former should be absolutely parallel and smooth. Finish with a broad-nosed tool and a very fine cut and turn the piston to suit.

With an engine of this type where the cylinder is open to the crankcase a certain amount of water inevitably gets into it, so a drain plug is provided as a means of getting rid of it.

This little engine is capable of quite a high performance, and if lubrication is properly attended to will remain free from wear for a very long time.

The engine shown in Fig. 20 is a much larger one than the foregoing, and is of the twin cylinder type with an overhead piston valve serving both cylinders. The crankshaft and the return crank, which takes the place of the more usual eccentric and drives the valve, are of the ball-bearing type. The engine, as detailed, is not a uniflow, but if anyone prefers this type, then all that is necessary is to provide a belt of ports as separately detailed and to lengthen the piston valve heads as shown so that they do not at any time uncover the ports at their outer edges. The exhaust holes in the piston valve housing would, of course, in such event be unnecessary.

This engine is eminently suitable for driving a dynamo, centrifugal pump, or a canoe or light rowing boat. The nuts of the big end bolts should have split pins or wire passed through them to prevent any possibility of their working loose.

These single acting engines are very sweet running, as the pressure on the piston, connecting-rod, and crankpin is always in one direction.

I have actually seen an engine of this type fixed up to run with a pair of " vee " blocks used as temporary crankshaft bearings, there being no mechanical means whatever of holding down the crankshaft, and it functioned perfectly.

Fig. 21 depicts a twin cylinder double acting engine of the normal slide-valve type designed primarily for model marine work. In this case the cylinders are separated entirely from the crankcase and the access from them to it of condensed water is practically impossible.

This engine is capable of driving a fine lined boat up to at least 6 ft. 0 in. long (always assuming the provision of a suitable boiler and proper firing arrangement) or a boat of the tug type of 4 ft. 0 in. to 4 ft. 6 in. In the case of the latter type of boat I should strongly

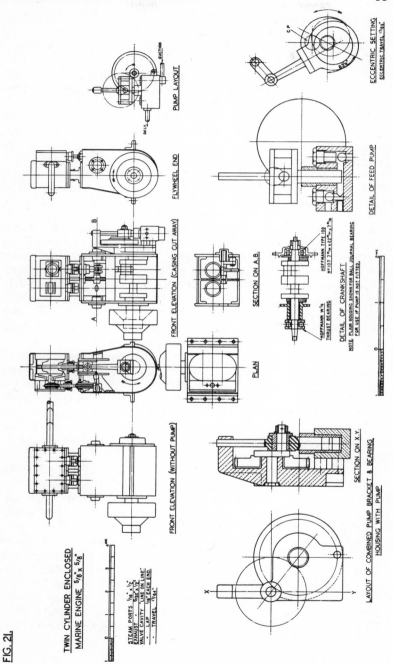

FIG. 21

TWIN CYLINDER ENCLOSED
MARINE ENGINE ⁵/₈" x ⁵/₈"

STEAM PORTS ¹/₁₆" x ¹/₂"
EXHAUST — ³/₃₂" x¹/₂"
VALVE CAVITY — ⁵/₁₆" ON LINE
LAP — ¹/₁₆" EACH END
TRAVEL — ¹⁷/₆₄"

PUMP LAYOUT

FLYWHEEL END

FRONT ELEVATION (CASING CUT AWAY)

FRONT ELEVATION (WITHOUT PUMP)

ECCENTRIC SETTING
ECCENTRIC TRAVEL ¹⁷/₆₄"

DETAIL OF FEED PUMP

SECTION ON A.B.

DETAIL OF CRANKSHAFT
NOTE PLAIN HOUSING SHOWN FOR BALL JOURNAL BEARING
FOR USE IF PUMP IS NOT FITTED.

HOFFMANN TYPE 100
N°107 ⁷·⁹/₁₆ x 2·²⁵/₃₂ x ⁷/₃₆

HOFFMANN w/₈
THRUST BEARING

PLAN

SECTION ON X.Y.

LAYOUT OF COMBINED PUMP BRACKET & BEARING
HOUSING WITH PUMP

recommend the introduction of a plain spur gear reduction to the propeller shaft of the order of 3 to 1 as thereby you will be able to use your available power through a much larger and more efficient propeller.

This engine is another of the family that lends itself admirably to building up to the almost total elimination of castings. The double throw crankshaft is made with circular webs and with reasonable care is not too difficult to make.

The only split bearings are the connecting-rod big ends which are of the marine type. As with all the engines described in this book, bearings throughout are of ample size.

The arrangement of the valve faces, steam-chests, and valves at the side of the cylinders ensures a very short and compact engine and to a degree simplifies pipe connections. The cylinders are intended to be of hard gunmetal with soft packed pistons, as it is only intended to use a moderate degree of superheat. So far as pressure is concerned, the engine could quite safely be worked at anything up to 150 lb. per sq. in., but unless the last ounce of power is required I should recommend 80 to 90 lb. Where only low power is wanted 50 lb. would be perfectly satisfactory. Large ports and passages are incorporated and the valve proportions specified will give 75 per cent. cut off and a full opening to exhaust. The vital necessity of a free exhaust is insufficiently appreciated where any sort of reasonable efficiency is required.

To provide excessive lead and in addition exhaust clearance is an unsatisfactory and inefficient solution to a problem, which lends itself to being solved by much more scientific and efficient means. For any ordinary model steam engine, if it is properly designed and made exhaust clearance is not only totally unnecessary, but definitely harmful to thermal efficiency. For all ordinary model work where a slide or piston valve is used, the exhaust should be arranged " line and line."

The sketches referred to in Chapter 3, z, z1 and z2 will make clear what is meant by " exhaust clearance."

To quote such authorities as the late Henry Greenly, the late G. S. Willoughby, or Henry Muncaster, all qualified *practical* engineers, " the necessity for exhaust clearance to enable an engine to function properly is a sign of faulty design elsewhere." The many years during which I earned my living helping to build, erect, test, and maintain, and finally designing steam engines, which had to give commercially satisfactory results if I was to continue to hold my job, amply confirm this view. It is a fact that in many engines with heavy working parts, and high piston speeds, it was regular practice to apply " exhaust lap " to ensure sufficient compression to absorb the inertia forces generated by the reciprocating masses. This, of course, is never necessary in model work where inertia forces are naturally usually so small as to be safely disregarded.

A geared pump is detailed (the normal speed of the engine should be of the order of 1,500-2,000 r.p.m., which is too high for the efficient working of an ordinary pump) and it is driven by means of a small crankpin working in a Scotch yoke, an arrangement often referred to as a slide crank. The peculiar setting of the hole in the slide block is intentional. The crank pin can be fixed in any one of four holes in the driving gear, which acts as a crank disc, each hole giving a different stroke. The slide block is square and can be inserted in the yoke in any one of four positions. Each position corresponds to a hole in the crank disc and by correct placing, whatever stroke is chosen for the pump, the plunger will always go practically to the bottom of the pump barrel, thus avoiding any risk of air locks. The device gives four ranges of feed and is much simpler than any normal variable feed arrangement. Lubrication to cylinders and valves is taken care of by a large displacement lubricator.

It will be noted that a ball thrust bearing is housed between the flywheel and the main bearing; this, of course, is only required where a direct driven propeller is coupled to the engine without the intervention of a separate thrust block. At the forward end a ball-bearing is used but for those who prefer it a plain bearing, exactly similar to that at the propeller end can be used, in fact, if boiler feeding arrangements are such as not to require the engine-driven feed-pump, I should recommend this procedure as the simpler (and cheaper !).

As a matter of fact an engine based on this general layout, but modified to incorporate Hackworth, Bremme, or Marshall valve-gear and increased four times would make an excellent little launch engine for river work (for sea work one requires a *condensing* engine and preferably a compound or triple expansion at that). Such an engine would be capable of developing 10 to 12 b.h.p. quite comfortably and being totally enclosed should result in a very neat and quiet running engine.

CHAPTER 9

A PINNACE TYPE ENGINE

WHERE AN engine is required to combine a high power-weight ratio with good wearing qualities and general robustness of construction, the pinnace type of twin cylinder or compound engine is hard to beat.

Fig. 22, details 1 to 9, show such an engine in its twin cylinder form. In the days when pinnaces, launches, and admiral's barges were steam driven, engines of this general type were made by a number of marine engineering firms and differed from one another only in details. All were characterised by robust construction and large bearing surfaces, which gave them a capacity to stand up to hard work for long periods.

This model makes use of castings for the baseplate and cylinders. As will be seen the cylinders are supported on six steel columns which are themselves stayed together in both longitudinal and transverse directions.

The crossheads are not in accordance with usual full size practice, but of a modified form simpler to make and just as efficient in use. The guide bars are carried at their upper ends by lugs on the bottom cylinder covers and at their lower ends by a cross beam, itself bolted to the three back columns. The crankshaft is made from the solid and would require a billet of mild steel of good quality, say, $1\frac{5}{8}$ in. diameter by 6 in. long. The cranks are balanced. The extra thickness of the portion of the webs forming the balance weights may be made from separate plates riveted to the web, or from the solid. The latter is the more satisfactory job but involves rather more complicated operations in turning. It will be noted that very large bearing surfaces are provided both for the crankpins and main journals.

Three bearings are provided for the crankshaft and these are of the split brass type square sided and flanged, and retained in place by simple flat steel caps, themselves retained by studs and locknuts.

The eccentrics have large wearing surfaces and a central web to keep the strap in place. They should preferably be made from centrifugally-cast iron bar, and straps of the same material are ideal. Cast-iron eccentrics and cast-iron straps are an important exception

56

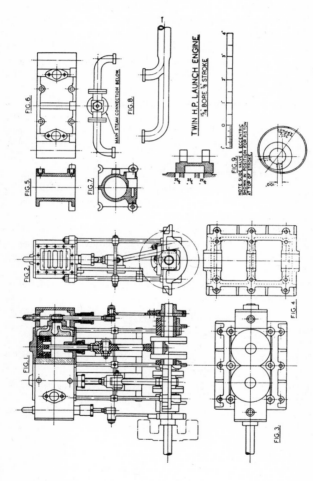

FIG. 6

FIG. 8

MAIN STEAM CONNECTION BELOW.

TWIN H.P. LAUNCH ENGINE
1¼ BORE ⅞ STROKE

FIG. 5

FIG. 7

FIG. 9
NOTE. SLIDE VALVE & ECCENTRIC
SHOWN IN POSITION FOR PISTON
AT TOP OF STROKE.

FIG. 2

FIG. 4

FIG. 1

FIG. 3

FIG. 22.

to the general rule that similar metals should not work in sliding or revolving contact one with another.

Failing cast iron, steel eccentrics and hard gunmetal straps are a perfectly satisfactory alternative. As has been stressed before, the eccentrics should be a first class fit on the crankshaft.

The connecting rods have the normal marine type of big end and an eye little end. The big end is fitted with gunmetal or phosphor bronze brasses and locknutted bolts; note in this connection that contrary to what one so often sees the *lock nut* should be the *inner* one and the thick nut the *outer* one. It is the *outer* nut that carries the strain.

The little end is thoroughly case-hardened and works on a case-hardened wrist pin. The crossheads have a separate back cover studded and nutted to the main body, the wrist pins being nutted into the crosshead and held tight. A tiny pin should be set through the head and into the crosshead face to prevent the pin rotating. The piston rods are screwed into the crossheads with a fine thread (40 t.p.i.) and lock-nutted. Two flats are made just behind this thread so that the rod may be turned by a small spanner. It is essential that the tapped hole in the crosshead is kept square and lineable with the guide faces; this is most important. Looking at Fig. 2 the engine is intended to rotate clockwise and a moment's consideration will show that under these conditions, the thrust of the crosshead is constantly to the left on to its solid face.

If for any reason it is desired that the engine should give opposite rotation, turn it end for end; as it is completely symmetrical this makes no difference at all. Unless the crankshaft is made with an extension at each end, this would have to be set up end for end from the manner shown in Fig. 1.

Turning to the cylinders, these have been designed to give a high cylinder performance. Piston heads are long and as shown carry two rings of $\frac{3}{16}$ in. sq. braided soft packing each. Those with sufficient skill can fit light piston rings, and if cast iron is used for the cylinders this is preferable; in such case the pistons should be built up to avoid the necessity of springing on the rings. Ports, *and passages*, are of ample size, as is the exhaust cavity in the slide valve. These features are absolutely essential to any engine from which a high performance combined with a reasonable degree of efficiency is required. This is not hot air or theory but sound and proved practice agreed and followed by steam engineers the world over for at least 125 years.

It will be noted that both the piston rod glands and the valve rod glands are long and have considerable capacity for packing, note also that the faces of gland and stuffing box are square-ended, *not* bevelled. The glands are of a type largely used in small power engines and give highly satisfactory working results, they should only be tightened just sufficiently to prevent leakage, anything more than this merely leads to unnecessary friction, and, if excessive, to wear on the rods.

The valve-rods are extended through dummy glands, which, in conjunction with the long live gland, obviates any necessity for an external valve rod guide. The valve-rods drive the valves through threaded blocks which float in the jaws on the back of the valves. The outer end of the valve-rod has a little crosshead screwed on to it and is lock-nutted. The thread in the driving nuts is 40 t.p.i., $\frac{3}{16}$ in. and that in the crossheads 2-B.A. 31·4 t.p.i. This gives a differential adjustment to the valve and makes really accurate valve-setting a simple matter. It is my own practice first to set the valves as accurately as possible by sight and to make final adjustments with the engine under steam by ear, and I find this most satisfactory.

For holding on steam-chests and covers, and cylinder covers, studs and nuts are to be preferred to setscrews, 6-B.A. is a suitable size. Joints can be made with oiled brown paper. This engine is capable of continuous hard work and may be run at anything up to 2,000 r.p.m. with steam up to 125 lb. per sq. in.

Under such conditions it would give in the region of 1 b.h.p. On the other hand it will be perfectly satisfactory with steam at 50 to 60 lb. per sq. in.

In any case a moderate degree of superheat is desirable. It will be noted that both steam and exhaust pipes are of ample size and it is proposed to use a " cross " wheel valve, with the wheel on top and the steam inlet beneath, to control the steam supply. A large displacement lubricator feeding direct into the valve body *above* the valve is recommended.

Piston and valve rods should be of stainless steel, crossheads, connecting rods, and eccentric rods of mild steel and guide bars of cast steel, in the form known as " ground-stock " or " gauge-plate." In such matters as lagging the maker can follow his fancy, the earlier engines had the cylinders lagged with mahogany strips held on by brass bands, the latter types had blued lagging steel screwed on direct, and in passing, this is one of the few places where slot-headed (round head) screws are in order but for heaven's sake keep them small, around 12 B.A. is about right for an engine of this size; nothing looks worse than great fat headed screws in such locations; it is careful attention to little details of this nature that make all the difference between the model which wins awards at exhibitions and the one the judges regularly pass by. Where weight is of importance the balance wheel may be abolished, but where it is not so important the balance wheel will assist steady running at slow speeds. Fig. 14 (see p. 32, Chapter 5) gives details of a pair of compound cylinders as an alternative. Unless a pressure of around 100 lb. or more is available there is nothing to be gained by compounding and I personally favour the simple for this type and size.

Fig. 15 (see p. 32, Chapter 5) gives details of valves and eccentric settings for the compound based on a working pressure of about 120 lb.

Of course, where used for marine propulsion the originals of this type of engine all had reversing gear, almost universally of the Stephenson link motion type (more correctly, Howe type, for he was the inventor) but for a model intended to propel a boat there is nothing whatever to be gained by fitting this, it adds a lot to the work involved, creates added friction and wear, and is of no practical use. Where radio control is intended recovery gear, of course, adds considerably to the fun of operating and obviously extends greatly the manoeuvres which can be carried out.

An engine built to these drawings would be capable of propelling a boat of reasonably fine lines up to 8 ft. 0 in. or 9 ft. 0 in. long and perfectly satisfactory for a 5 ft. 0 in.- 5 ft. 6 in. tug or trawler.

Once again for the latter type of work I would recommend a reduction drive to the propeller shaft of between 2 and 3 to 1.

CHAPTER 10

A SINGLE CYLINDER HIGH DUTY MARINE ENGINE

THE ENGINE illustrated in Fig. 23 is of a type eminently suited to marine work where a simple, robust, and thoroughly reliable engine is wanted in conditions where weight saving is not of first importance. Whilst the engine is not unduly heavy, it is certainly not a lightweight job and no attempt has been made at weight-saving. Castings are required for the cylinder, steam-chest and cover, trunk guide and baseplate.

This design utilises a circular crosshead and bored guide, a type which is naturally conducive to accurate alignment and free running and one largely used in small high power steam engine practice, as, for instance, in the famous White and Doble steam car engines. The cylinder is designed with a built on port face, a method of construction which enables clean smooth steam passages to be made where coring would be, if not impracticable, at least unlikely to be satisfactory. It is intended that the cylinder should be made of gunmetal and so there will be no difficulty in silver soldering on to it, the separate gunmetal port face.

This method gives excellent results in practice. I have used it in at least a dozen engines, and it gives far more efficient results than the wretched rows of drilled holes of inadequate size so popular with a certain school of design. I did not originate it; that was done over 45 years ago by a very talented model engineer, the late Henry Lea, of Birmingham. *

The crankshaft is detailed as a built-up press fit job, but those who prefer it can just as well machine it from the solid. As will be seen it is of the balanced type and it has generous scantlings throughout.

The base or bed is a casting and houses the two split main bearings in square sided recesses, the brasses being retained by plain steel caps themselves held down by studs and lock-nuts. The bottom of the base is closed and serves as a crank-race, if a couple of light sheet metal splash guards are fixed, one on each side on the top of the base and reaching to the flange of the trunk guide they will save a lot of oil being slung around the engine room.

---

* I have since discovered that the method was used by the late Henry Greenly 57 years ago!

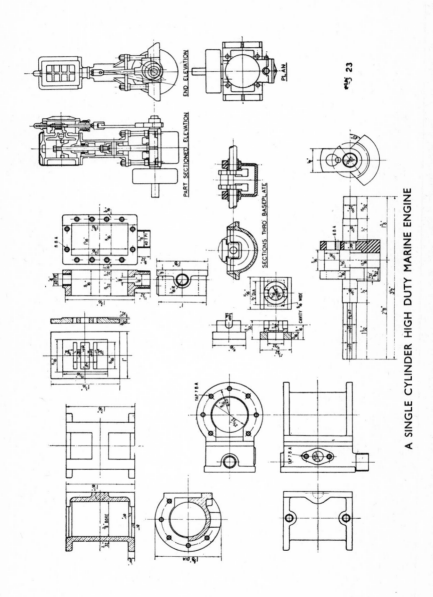

A SINGLE CYLINDER HIGH DUTY MARINE ENGINE

CHAPTER 11

A 3 in. SCALE LAUNCH ENGINE

THIS ENGINE differs from all the other designs in the book inasmuch as it is a model of an actual engine.

In the early years of this century, I was employed as a draughts-man in the firm with whom I had served my apprenticeship. During my apprenticeship and for a year or two after, whilst still in the shops I had had a pretty wide experience of steam engines in wide variety. I was given the job of designing a launch engine for use on rivers and lakes in tugs, workboats, etc. My instructions were to produce a robust single cylinder non-condensing engine with large bearing surfaces and good provision for lubrication. The engine illustrated in Plates 9-11 is an exact 3 in. scale model of the one I designed (a considerable number of which were built and sold) and incidentally was awarded a Championship Cup and the Bradbury Winter Cup at the Model Engineer Exhibition of 1959-60. It was not a vintage year for the " General " class and the Championship was an easy one, but I was very proud of the Bradbury Winter Cup (a) because it was awarded for " the most outstanding example of amateur craftsmanship " and (b) because I had a very great admiration for the charming and talented gentleman in whose memory the Cup was given.

The original engine was 6 in. bore, 5 in. stroke, suitable for working at anything from 90-120 lb. per sq. in. steam pressure, and running at anything up to 600-650 r.p.m. and developing, dependent on working pressure and speed, from 20 to 30 h.p.

It differed from the usual run of launch engines in one or two respects; it had a much longer connecting rod, relative to the stroke, than usual, in order to obtain a sweeter-running engine and reduced loading on the crosshead, whilst instead of the usual launch engine slotted link, it had marine type double bar links. These are more expensive to make, but if properly designed give an absolute mini-mum of " link slip " and have very large wearing surfaces. A feed-water-heater of the concentric return tube type was embodied and effected a marked economy in fuel consumption. The bearing surfaces throughout were of most generous proportions. Cylinder lubrication was taken care of by a large displacement lubricator

Plate 9.   A 3 in. scale launch engine

which combined the features of the Nathan and the Roscoe. A short cardan shaft was provided between engine and thrust block to take up any misalignment caused through the " working " of the hull, due to dampness or strains.   The rear universal joint was of the usual " Hooke " form, the front one of the form now known as the Hardy Spicer, but using a flexible laminated metal ring in place of the Hardy Spicer rubberized fabric ring.   Reversing was by a bent handle and double threaded screw, again unusual in a small launch engine, where normally a lever was used. Removeable splash guards were fitted each side of the crank race and a closed sheet metal sump beneath it with a pipe and drain cock. A drain cock was fitted to the bottom of the steam chest, and a single drain cock controlled both cylinder drains, pipes from these were taken to the sump. The crankshaft was of the balanced built-up force fit type.

Plate 9a.   A 3 in. scale launch engine

A large capacity lubricator fitted to the end of the gudgeon pin took care of both big and little ends of the connecting rod which was hollow, with the normal marine type big end. The gudgeon pin was fixed in the crosshead, case hardened as was also the little end. The crosshead was of a type which at the time I fondly imagined to be original, only to find out years later that Messrs. Sissons had been using it for years earlier! That taught me to be very chary of claiming priority for any ideas, or shooting a line that " I done it first ".

As stated, the model shown in the photographs is an exact copy of the original, but the set of drawings were slightly modified in minor details, notably as regards the feedwater heater, which in its original form entailed a great deal of work, and in the cylinder lubricator, but in general they follow the original almost exactly.

Plate 9b.   A 3 in. scale launch engine

The only casting on my model was the cylinder body, which was a Stuart Turner 1½ in. by 1¼ in. and which only required the ports and passages slightly enlarging to fill the bill. Everything else was either built up or cut from the solid.   Two light section cast iron piston rings were fitted on the built-up piston, and packing glands were of large capacity with full-floating stuffing bushes.   The drawings are fully detailed, they were traced from my originals by Mrs. Steel of Greenly Engineering Models, from whom incidentally full sized blueprints can be obtained.

The cylinder and steam chest were lagged with sheet aluminium, at the time the engine was built a material coming into fashion; my personal preference today would be either mahogany or teak strips over felt or flannel, or blued lagging steel.

As a working model, one made to the same size as my own would be capable of driving quite a large boat, say a liner or other reasonably fine lined type up to at least 10 ft. 0 in. long. It would in fact be capable of driving a two-seater canoe, but, in my opinion canoes in the smaller sizes are far from ideal as power craft.

A model built to $1\frac{1}{2}$ in. to 1 ft. 0 in. scale, half the size of the one illustrated, would make up quite satisfactorily, the cylinder size working out at $\frac{3}{4}$ in. bore $\frac{5}{8}$ in. stroke.

As an alternative the engine would make a good non-reversing stationary engine in either size and drawings are included for the necessary modifications. If so made a shaft governor actuating a balanced throttle valve would be a great improvement.

CHAPTER 12

TWIN OSCILLATING PADDLE ENGINES

THE SET of engines illustrated herewith have some claims to originality. As already pointed out the rotational speed required by the paddles in a model is far too low to allow of even comparative efficiency in the engine, and this applies with equal force to a model of the usual " modern " diagonal slide valve engines. On looking into the engine-room of most model paddle steamers one finds either direct acting engines, which must in the nature of things be inefficient, or something embodying gear reduction which whilst it may be more efficient than the direct acting type, resembles nothing that ever was on land or sea. An accurate scale model of a set of oscillating paddle engines is a very big undertaking indeed, as will be realised by those who have seen the magnificent model made by the late Engineer Commander Barker, R.N., or some of the engines of this type in the Science Museum. It is certainly a quite impractical proposition as a working model in the smaller sizes. The set of engines illustrated in the drawings is in the nature of a compromise, and is an attempt to produce a reasonably efficient power plant which in appearance will retain the broad characteristics of the type without embodying excessive complication. The inherent drawback to the oscillating engine in which the steam distribution is controlled by the to and fro swing of the cylinders is got over by the use of simple plate distributing valves, eccentric driven, and the rotational speed drawback by building into the engine a four to one concentric reduction gear to each paddle wheel, thus allowing the engine to attain a reasonable revolution speed, whilst the paddle wheels too can rotate at a speed not unreasonably " out of scale ". The hull to accommodate these engines requires a minimum beam of 8 in. which, accepting the normal proportions for a pleasure steamer means an overall length of something between 5 ft. 0 in. and 6 ft. 6 in.

The engines are not condensing, though they could be made so without too much added complication, but unless it is intended to operate in salt water, it is not in my opinion a worthwhile proposition. In any case, a fine lined and comparatively lightly built vessel of this type is not really suited for operation on any but sheltered waters.

The air pump on such engines was usually driven either by a short throw crank or a large eccentric placed centrally on the crankshaft. In this model this is replaced by an eccentrically operated boiler feed pump and the condenser by an exhaust feedwater heater. The general effect is an engine very similar in appearance to the full-sized article.

Both pump and feedwater heater can be omitted if desired, as if a Scotch boiler with a reasonable water capacity is used feed water problems can be taken care of by an injector, a hand pump, or a donkey pump. However, for those who don't mind the extra work involved, the pump and feedwater heater are worthwhile, as the latter will substantially reduce the work of the boiler and lessen the amount of feedwater required. The plate valves operate in exactly the same manner as an ordinary slide valve and the steam distribution is in no way different from that in a normal slide valve cylinder: the swing of the cylinder has no effect on the steam distribution at all, this being controlled entirely by the valve itself.

It might be thought that the plate valves would result in considerable added friction, but actually this is not so, as they move only slightly out of phase with the cylinders. The two reduction gear housings form in effect the main crankshaft bearings. The actual reduction gears take the form of a lathe back gear, and as previously stated give a reduction of 4 to 1 (or if you prefer it that way 1 to 4!). There are only two sizes of gears all of 30 d.p. and it is suggested that the simplest way to make them is to take a piece of bar stock for each size long enough to allow of parting off four wheels or pinions and cut the teeth on the stock before parting, thus you are sure that all four wheels and all four pinions will be identical in pitch diameter. Note that the second-motion pinions have extended sleeves to carry the first reduction wheels, and you must of course allow for this in your stock. Obviously the best course is to reduce the stock at each end to the diameter of the sleeve, which will save you cutting an extra tooth length. An allowance of $\frac{1}{8}$ in. full for each parting should be sufficient to allow of a trimming skim on each face. The first reduction gears should be a driving fit on the second motion pinion sleeves, and pinned thereto by $\frac{1}{16}$ in. pegs half in the sleeve and half in the gearwheel bore. The first reduction pinions and the final drive gears should be similarly fixed to the crankshaft and paddle shafts respectively.

The pinions may be of hard phosphor bronze or gunmetal, or good mild steel, in the latter case the dead layshaft should be case-hardened. The wheels should preferably be of phosphor bronze or gunmetal, but there is no serious objection to their being of mild steel. Two points are of vital importance in connection with the cylinders. First the trunnions must be exactly at right angles to the centre-line of the cylinder bore and their axis must intersect the said centre-line. Also, of course, they must both be on the same axis and the port face machined truly accurately at right angles to that axis.

Secondly the layout and cutting of the ports must be accurate, as equally must it be in the distributing plate valves and the steam block. Too much care cannot be taken over these points, as they are of the utmost importance to the efficient functioning of the engine. The pump drive is so arranged that the stroke can be adjusted to suit the requirements of the boiler. This is done in such a way that the ram is always in the same position at the delivery end of the stroke, thus maintaining a minimum clearance. The method of keeping the port faces of the cylinders, the plate valves and the steam block faces in close contact should reduce friction to a minimum.

As the trunnions support the cylinders on both sides, there is no reaction trying to tilt the cylinder away from the valve and thus all the spring is required to do is to maintain a steam-tight contact between the working faces. The crankshaft is built in two sections, held together by a sleeve, as it would be a somewhat flimsy job to make in one piece, and furthermore would require that the pump eccentric should be split, which in turn would necessitate increasing its size, which is already big enough! By the way, don't forget to put the eccentrics in place on the sleeve before assembling the crankshaft, elementary I know, but we can all slip up at times, at least *nearly* all! Faces of steam distribution block, plate valves and cylinder port faces should all be scraped to surface plate, and it is extremely important that the plate valves should be of perfectly even thickness throughout.

I think that about covers the high spots of the engine itself, and there is nothing in it to scare any reasonably competent model engineer who has got beyond the " hole poking " stage. As a paddle engine is incomplete without paddle wheels, a full set of details for these is provided.

There can be no question that feathering wheels are very much more efficient than are fixed paddle radial wheels, and this extra efficiency is probably quite as marked in a model as in the full-sized article, so feathering wheels it is.

These are based on those designed by the late Wm. Stroudley for his cross-Channel steamers back in the early 80s of the last century. Of course, there is a very great deal more work in feathering wheels than in plain radial wheels but if you don't like work, better give up model engineering and go fishing. One of the snags encountered with working model paddle steamers with feathering wheels is that the fixed eccentric pin, which operates the feathering gear, is mounted upon the sponson, and said sponson is somewhat vulnerable, and if damaged may wreck, or at least seriously derange the whole of the feathering gear. To get over this I have arranged that the whole of the paddle gear is self contained. It is carried on a long sleeve, itself fixed by a flange directly to the reduction gear case. At its outer end it carries a horizontal steel plate arm, at the outer ends of which are two steel distance pieces which clear the paddle blades, and in turn at their outer ends carry a second stretcher, outside the paddle wheels, on which is mounted, adjustably, the pin which controls the feathering gear. This framing is entirely hidden by the sponsons proper, which are quite clear of it, and by the paddle boxes, and so no objection arises on the grounds of appearances. The arrangement largely minimises risks of accidental damage and it ensures that engines, paddle shafts, paddles and feathering gear become a single unit, quite independent of the hull.

Considering the paddles, the blades, or perhaps more usually floats, should be made from hard sheet brass of about 20 S.W.G. and it would probably be well worthwhile making up a pair of wood formers, male and female, and using the vice to operate them, to ensure that the whole 18 are alike, a point which is, to say the least, highly desirable.

A lot of the work is of a repetition nature and will give the executant an opportunity for using his ingenuity in developing "production" methods. Paddle wheel frames, spokes, brackets, etc., should be made from sheet brass, in fact apart from spindles, joint pins and distance pieces, which should be of stainless steel, brass is the material to be used throughout. Pins and axles, etc., should all be an easy fit, which does not mean a lot of slackness. There are so many joints that any tightness can lead to the absorption of a lot of power.

The total width of the boat over paddle-boxes, allowing for good hefty sponsons, which I suggest should be made of hard angle brass, will come out between $16\frac{1}{2}$ in. and 17 in.

As regards boiler power I would suggest a "dryback" Scotch boiler about 5 in. diameter by $6\frac{1}{2}$ in. overall length (including combustion chamber) with a $2\frac{1}{4}$ in. furnace and about $28\frac{5}{16}$-in. diameter return tubes, which will provide ample steam. A coil superheater in the combustion chamber giving 12-14 sq. in. of heating surface would be a worthwhile improvement and would pep up performance. The Scotch boiler is a fast steamer, has a low centre of gravity and a good water capacity ; of all "tank" types it is probably the best for model marine work. Working pressure 45-50 lb./sq. in.

It is realised that these engines will not appeal to everybody as they are well away from the usual run, but anybody who takes the trouble to build a set will I think be pleased with the result, and if he installs it in a boat, he will not be shy of letting anyone look into his engine room, whilst in running it will almost certainly be a good deal more efficient than the standard slow-running types.

A small vertical engine was built to try out the plate valve arrangement and proved successful. It utilises a cylinder valve and steam block identical with those in this design, except that the steam block is single-sided and the cylinder inverted. In conclusion 1 ought to say that so far as I know the plate valve idea was originated by Mr. J. L. Beilschmidt, see ME 22/3/34.

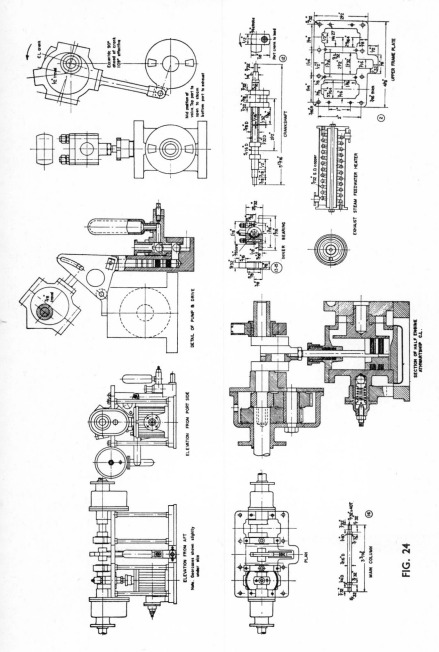

FIG. 24

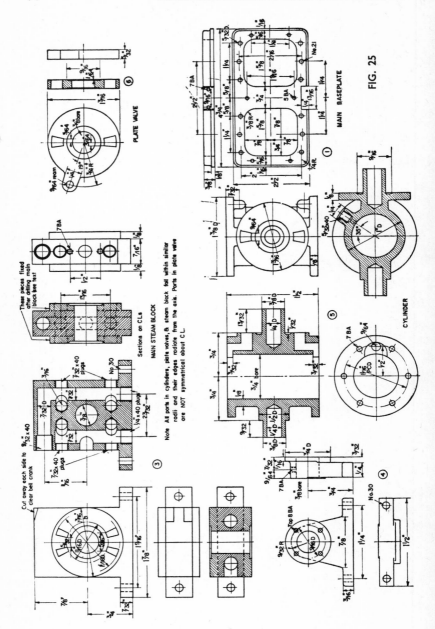

FIG. 25

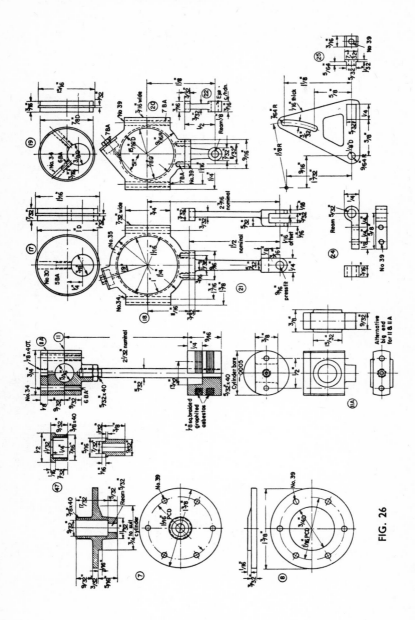

FIG. 26

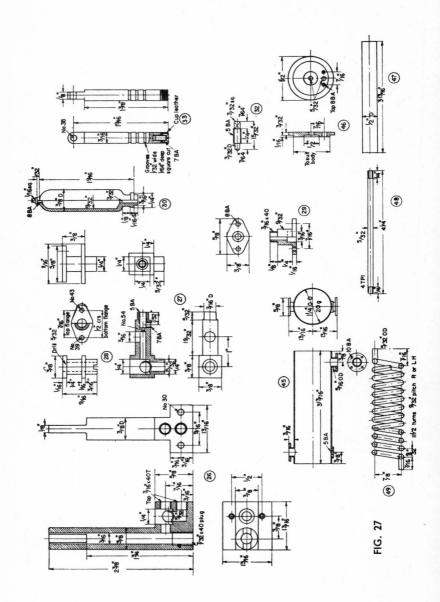

FIG. 27

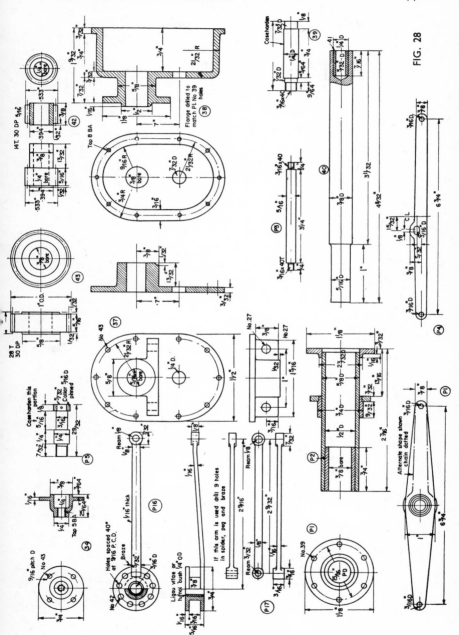

FIG. 28

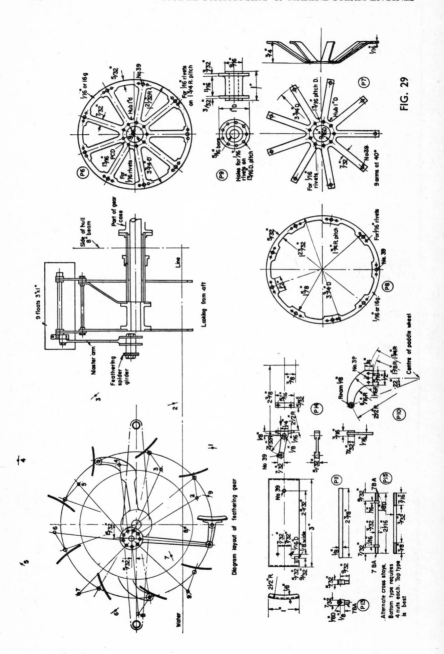

FIG. 29

CHAPTER 13

CYLINDER DESIGN AND CONSTRUCTION

THE HEAT energy of the steam produced by the boiler is converted into useful work by the engine, and the essential component in this conversion is the engine cylinder together with its piston. Slide (or piston) valve, valve gear, motion work, etc., are all ancillary to this; the cylinder is the heart of the matter. Unless the cylinder is efficiently designed, accurately made and properly and continuously lubricated with a correct grade of cylinder oil, it will not matter how good everything else is, you cannot possibly attain reasonable efficiency. This being the case it has been thought well to devote a complete chapter to the question of cylinder design and construction.

In the first place a moment's consideration will serve to show that the more freely the steam can enter the cylinder, and when it has done its work, get away to the atmosphere (or the condenser in a condensing engine) the less will be the frictional losses and the losses due to back pressure in the exhaust line, which of course retard or tend to retard the piston, and reduce the mean effective pressure, which incidentally is always much less than the boiler pressure. To attain the optimum results ports and passages must be of adequate size and as free from sharp bends, corners and angles as practical considerations will permit, so we will start by considering suitable proportions. Fig. 30 shows diagrammatically a typical cylinder for a horizontal engine. " D " is the diameter of the bore, and experience has shown that it is sound practice to base port and passage sizes on this dimension.

It may at first sight be thought that stroke too should be considered, but actually in practice this is unnecessary for the reason that, speaking generally, long-stroke engines run at a lower *revolution* speed than do short-stroke engines, and taken all round piston speed, which is what matters in this connection, does not vary much with length of stroke.

If we take " D " as representing the bore of the cylinder, the

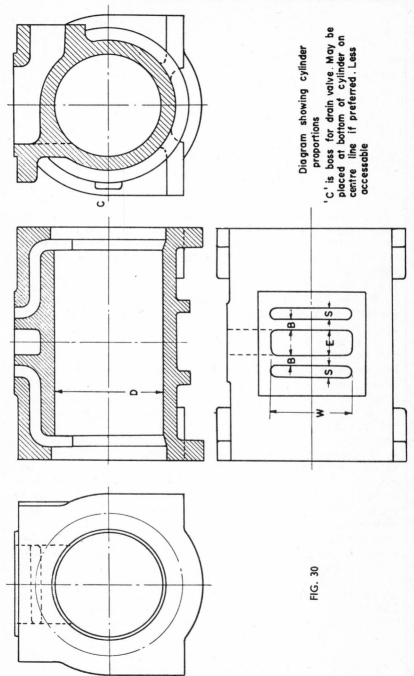

Diagram showing cylinder proportions

'C' is boss for drain valve. May be placed at bottom of cylinder on centre line if preferred. Less accessable

FIG. 30

following formula will be found to give excellent practical results.

$$D = \text{Cylinder Bore}$$
$$S = \frac{D}{10}$$
$$B = \frac{D}{10}$$
$$E = \frac{D}{4}$$
$$W = D \times \cdot 75 \text{ to } D \times \cdot 875.$$

With reference to " W " the larger proportion should be adopted where high piston speed is contemplated. (In actual fact very few models indeed have anything approaching high piston speeds; a 2 in. × 2 in. engine running at 2,000 r.p.m. which would be exceptionally high, will have a piston speed of less than 700 ft. per min.: I have seen a reversing rolling mill engine, with a stroke of 5 ft. 0 in. running at 200 r.p.m., giving a piston speed of 2,000 ft. per min. It is safe to say that few double acting model engines ever exceed a piston speed of 500 ft. per min.) The length " B " of the port bars is not very important, but keeping it equal to the port length gives a satisfactory proportion. *The passages between port face and cylinder bore should be maintained throughout their length at the full cross-sectional area of the port.* Actually in full size practice they are usually a little larger and are generally increased at the bends to make things easier for the steam. The popular arrangement of providing a port with a face area of say ·171 sq. in. and then providing four No. 30 drilled holes each with a couple of near right-angled sharp cornered bends has no merits at all except that it is " easy ". (The figures given, by the way, are actually taken from a design for a model locomotive, published in the *M.E.* some years ago.) The relative areas of port and passage are approximately as 1 to $\frac{1}{4}$. The walls of the drilled holes present a very large surface area relative to their cross section. Actually the periphery of the port is 2·43 in. and its area ·171 sq. in., a ratio of approximately 14 to 1; four No. 30 holes have a combined periphery of 1·60 in. and an area of ·05 sq. in., a ratio of 32 to 1, and their right-angled bends do nothing to assist matters!

The usual arguments put forward in support of this thoroughly bad and inefficient procedure, apart from its being " easy ", run thus: " When the engine is working at short cut off the steam port is only partially opened and the small holes will pass all the necessary steam; furthermore, large passages waste enormous quantities of steam as they have to be filled with high pressure steam at each stroke which is entirely wasted as it does no useful work."

It would indeed be difficult to put so many complete fallacies in so few words.

Firstly it entirely ignores the inconvenient fact that though referred to as " steam " ports and passages, these in fact function for half their time as " exhaust " passages and ports. Now with any decently designed valve and valve gear layout the " steam " port is fully open to exhaust right up to mid-gear. In full size practice the exhaust port is usually made anything from 2 to 2½ times the area of the " steam " port (this has been standard practice ever since the slide valve first came into use). Now what earthly sense is there in starting the exhaust steam on its way out of the cylinder, after it has done its work, expanded its volume, lost much of its fluidity and mobility, via a miserable set of restricted drilled holes having a total cross section of less than ⅓ of that of the steam port and ⅙ or less of that of the exhaust port? Well may exhaust clearance on the valve " improve " matters in such a case, they certainly need improving. Regarding the equally fallacious steam wasting allegation, let us examine the facts. With proper design of valve and valve gear, there is in the steam cycle a compression stage at the end of the exhaust stroke, which raises the pressure in the clearance space up to something approaching steam chest pressure (in certain conditions it may well exceed it) and therefore the clearance spaces do *not* have to be refilled with high pressure steam at every stroke. Lastly, as to the steam contained in the passages doing no useful work, this too is as far off beat as the rest of the pontification. Any steam trapped in the port and passage when the slide valve closes the port is part and parcel of the cylinder content and by its expansion contributes to the work done on the piston and to allege otherwise is either to seek deliberately to mislead or to display abysmal ignorance—you can take your pick! As I said above, it would be hard to compress more fallacies into so few words.

Passages should be faired and streamlined as much as possible, though this is not too easy in small sizes. Where passages can be cored the matter is simple (so long as the moulder is skilled and conscientious) but where it cannot be done, a useful alternative is to adopt the form of construction illustrated in Fig. 31. This form of construction was used, I believe quite independently, more than sixty years ago, by two great model engineers, the late Hy Lea, M.I.M.E., and the late Hy Greenly. Anyhow, whoever invented it, it is an excellent scheme.

In this scheme the port face is made separate from the cylinder and attached to it after the steam passages have been milled out. If the cylinders are made of gunmetal, the false port face can be silver-soldered to the cylinder body.

In the *Model Engineer* for 22/7/09 there is an exellent article on the technique adopted in doing this by Hy Lea himself.

In the case of gunmetal cylinders it is best to rough machine only the cylinder body before the silver soldering operaticn, and finish machine after, as there is some risk of distortion taking place during the heating. Alternatively the false face can be fixed by countersunk screws, put in where they do not interfere with the slide valve, the joint being made with a *thin* paste of litharge and glycerine. This

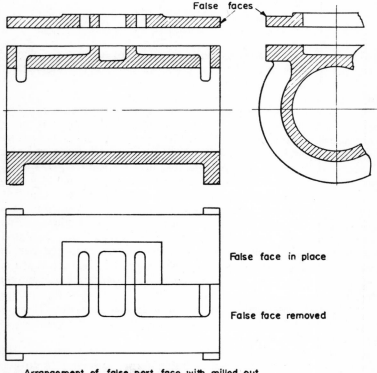

False faces

False face in place

False face removed

Arrangement of false port face with milled out steam and exhaust passages

FIG. 31

must be mixed just before it is required and used straight away, as it sets quite quickly, and like concrete, once this takes place it becomes useless and cannot be reconstituted.

With cast iron cylinders this form of construction is almost obligatory, though it is possible to silver solder cast iron it is a rather difficult proposition.

The ends of the cylinder bore should always be finished as shown in Fig. 32.

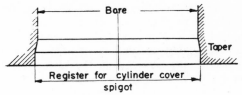

Detail of cylinder ends

FIG. 32

There are two reasons for this; (*a*) it makes it much simpler to insert the piston into the bore, whether it is fitted with soft packing or with rings, and (*b*) it allows of the cylinder being rebored without affecting the fit of the spigots on the cylinder covers. This is a point which is all too frequently neglected in model practice; it is so easy to take care of it when making the cylinders that there is really no excuse for failing to attend to it. The piston should *just* over-run the parallel bore at each end; if fitted with rings, the front ring and back ring (or top ring and bottom ring in a vertical engine) should each over-run the bore at its own end by not more than half its width.

The reason for this is to avoid the possibility of ridges forming at the ends of the bore. For similar reasons the working port face should stand proud of the joint face for the steam chest. This allows of refacing without affecting the position of this joint and thus altering the relative centres of piston rod and valve rod. Here again the length of the raised portion should be such that the ends of the slide valve just over-run it when operating at running cut-off.

The cylinder body, after finish-boring, should have a thickness of not less than $\frac{1}{8}$ " D ", whilst the flanges should have a thickness of from $\frac{1}{8}$ to $\frac{3}{16}$ " D ".

The width of the flanges should be about equal to three times the diameter of the studs (setscrews or bolts) used to fasten on the covers. Studs are best and should be used wherever possible and certainly for all cylinders over 1 in. bore.

The Table on page 93 gives the safe loading on B.A. studs, bolts or setscrews, of mild steel taken at a stress of 8,000 lb. per sq. in. on the *core* area. For gunmetal take half the figure for steel. Do *not* use silver steel for studs, etc., its structure is too " short " for this purpose. Monel metal is an excellent material, and for all practical purposes, non-corrosive; its strength may be taken as equivalent to steel.

In making calculations for cylinder cover and steam chest cover fastenings, take the full boiler pressure; in the case of cylinder covers allow a factor of safety of not less than 5 to take care of imponderable stresses arising from trapped water, for steam chest covers a factor of safety of 4 is ample.

As a very rough empirical guide for average conditions, for $\frac{1}{2}$ in. to $\frac{5}{8}$ in. bore cylinders use, say, 6 No. 8 B.A. studs, for $\frac{3}{4}$ in. to $\frac{7}{8}$ in. bore 6 No. 7 B.A.   1 in. to $1\frac{1}{8}$ in. 6 to 8 No. 7 B.A. $1\frac{1}{4}$ in. to $1\frac{1}{2}$ in. 8 No. 5 B.A. $1\frac{5}{8}$ in. to $1\frac{7}{8}$ in. 8 No. 4 B.A. or 12 No. 5 B.A.

Where unusually high working pressures are in question, say, 125 lb. sq. in. and upwards, it is safest to calculate each case in the light of the working conditions. , Of course the principles apply not only to steam chest covers, but to any other form of cover subject

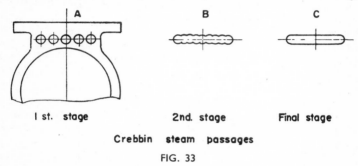

I st. stage   2nd. stage   Final stage

Crebbin   steam   passages

FIG. 33

to pressure.   If superheated high pressure steam is to be used (as with a flash generator) steel should be the material for studs and nuts, and it is a good idea to cover the threads with mercurial ointment prior to assembly as this prevents seizure; that is something I learned from steam car work more than fifty years ago.   Passages should be led into the cylinder barrel in the manner shown in "A" Fig. 34 and *not* as shown at "B" which is the method all too frequently adopted in model locomotive work.   The reason is that if done as in "B" the studs holding on the cylinder covers cannot be symmetrically spaced.

If for any reason the constructor decides to use the drilled passage scheme the method used by the late James Crebbin is a great improvement on the usual arrangement.   Fig. 33 shows how this is effected; "A" shows the spacing of the first lot of holes, spaced apart so that the outer edges of the outside holes coincide with the ends of the ports and spaces are left between the holes equal to about half their diameter.   When these holes are drilled cut off some lengths of brass rod which is an easy fit in the holes, tin them and insert them in the holes and sweat up; they should fill the holes from end to end and be filed off flush with the cylinder flange. Now put a centre pop in the middle of each " land " and drill a second set of holes, heat up and shake out the remains of the sweated-in rods and the resulting slot will look like " *B* ".   With a narrow flat file remove the higher portions of the ridges between the holes, or better still, file them flush with the bottoms of the holes.

The result will not be so good as with a cored or milled passage, but a very great deal better than the usual abortionate arrangement. Of course this method eliminates the possibility of making the cylinder as recommended at "*A* ", Fig. 34, but you can't have everything and make it " easy " at the same time!

Bosses for drain cocks or relief valves are usually arranged as shown in Fig. 36

Sometimes in addition to the hand-operated drain cocks, auto-

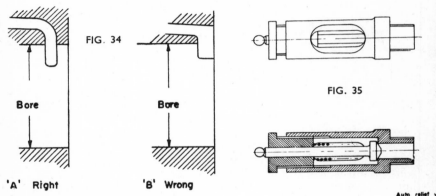

FIG. 34

Bore

Bore

'A' Right

'B' Wrong

Passages joining cylinder bore

FIG. 35

Auto relief valve

matic relief valves are fitted to the cylinder covers; they are in fact small direct loaded spring safety valves, intended to relieve pressure due to trapped water, they should be set to lift at about 5 lb. per sq. in. above boiler pressure. See fig. 35.

As a guide to size, they should have a clear bore of about 1/10 that of the cylinder.

In a horizontal engine they should be fitted as near the bottom edge of the cylinder covers as possible.

For cylinders of $1\frac{1}{4}$ in. bore and upwards, good quality cast iron is strongly recommended;better still " Meehanite " or nickel cast iron.

In use cast iron attains a glass-like surface of great hardness and low coefficient of friction.   If really superheated steam, as opposed to the more normal just dried variety, is to be used, cast iron is a must.   In 1 in. bore and over, pistons should be fitted with rings.

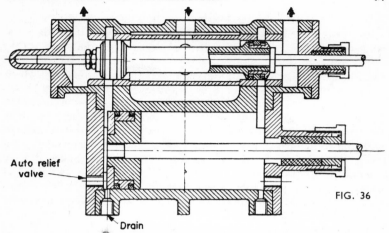

FIG. 36

Auto relief valve

Drain

Piston valve cylinder, ringed valve, and direct passages

These should be of light section, for 1 in. bore not exceeding a bare $\frac{1}{16}$ in. thick in the thickest part and $\frac{1}{16}$ in. or 5/64 in. wide, and may be made from centrifugally cast iron bush (a commercial article) or a good nickel steel. Below 2 in. bore, ringed pistons should always be built up in such a manner that the rings can be applied without having to spring them open, for in practice in the smaller sizes it is almost impossible to do this without either breaking or distorting them. Cast iron is probably the best piston material, but mild steel is also quite satisfactory. Where pistons are built up, the screws holding them together should be of gunmetal or monel metal, otherwise they may become rusted up solid and, short of drilling out, irremoveable. The port face should be kept as near the cylinder bore as practical conditions will permit, for reasons which will be obvious at a moment's consideration.

In my opinion there is no point in lapping the bore of either a G.M. or C.I. cylinder, if finished with a keen edged broad nosed boring tool with a light cut and a fine feed, after a few hours' running you will have a surface finish equal to anything you can attain by lapping. If you *do* decide to lap, do the job properly with a lead lap for non-ferrous cylinders and a copper lap for cast iron cylinders. Wrapping emery cloth round a broomstick and running it in the bore, is *not*, repeat *not*, lapping and even in skilled hands is apt to lead to inaccuracies in the bore; with a beginner it may easily prove disastrous; nobody who uses such methods has any claim to call himself an engineer or even a skilled mechanic.

Piston rods should preferably be of stainless steel (as too should valve rods) and their diameter should not be less than $\frac{1}{8}$ cylinder bore. Pistons should be finished turned upon their own rods, either with the rod held in an accurate collet or between centres, concentricity between piston and rod is most important.

Considering for a moment the steam chest, its cubic capacity cannot, within reason, be too large, as it is the reservoir from which the cylinder draws its steam at each stroke; a capacity equal to the swept capacity of the cylinder may be accepted as a desirable minimum. For those who have good milling equipment in their workshops,there is much to be said for casting the steam chest integral with the cylinder, but it does entail rather more difficult machining work than the usual separate steam chest and it makes it very difficult to scrape the valve face. In full size work it was not usual to scrape either port face or slide valve, the principle being that when warmed up a certain amount of distortion was inevitable which would negative the value of the scraping, and it was best to let things bed down on their own under working conditions. However in the sizes we are concerned with this hardly applies and I would recommend that both valve and port face be scraped to surface plate (a piece of plate glass makes an excellent substitute for a surface plate). Incidentally the minute depressions left by the scraper help to hold oil and so improve lubrication. As evidence of this I have always found that a properly scraped machine-tool slide works more easily and wears better than one finished by grinding or lapping. The scraper marks may well be of an order of depth of only $1/100,000$ in. but a molecule of oil is a lot smaller than that! When erecting an engine and fastening cylinder and steam chest covers in place, don't tighten up each nut and move on to the next, tighten one just moderately and then take one diametrically opposite to it and do the same, the next two should be again diametrically opposite each other and as far as possible spaced evenly between the first pair, carry on until all are partially tightened and then repeat tightening process in the same sequence. Oiled brown paper makes good jointing material for non-superheated steam up to, say, 100 lb. per sq. in. Above this use one of the proprietary sheet jointing materials such as " Klingerit ". For really high pressures and superheat use thin sheet copper, say, $1/64$ in. thick, thoroughly annealed before application. Make the holes for the fixing studs with a good clearance, as under pressure the holes tend to close in a little, and if made a fit in the first place it may be difficult to shift the copper jointing material without damaging it.

These copper joints have an almost indefinite life and can be used over and over again, but they should be re-annealed every time the joint is remade. The usual instruction for annealing copper is to make it a dull red hot and plunge into water.

The water part of the instruction has nothing to do with the annealing effect, it merely saves time; it also tends to distort the object, especially if of thin sheet, so in the case of the type of joint in question the advice is to make dull red hot and allow to cool naturally. The faces of pistons and cylinder covers should be polished, as this tends to reduce condensation. Where possible piston faces and the inside faces of the cover should be flat for similar reasons. Clearance at the ends should be kept down to the smallest safe limits, as an example a 2 in. stroke cylinder, if accurately made and assembled, can have a clearance between piston and cylinder cover of no more than 3/64 in. at each end. In this connection a screwed joint between piston rod and crosshead is a great advantage, besides which it is certainly the simplest and strongest method available. The fact that it was used in steam car engines by such

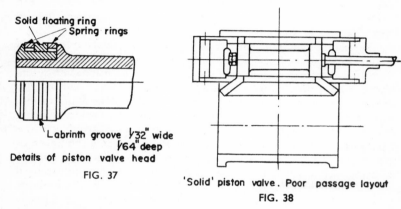

Solid floating ring
Spring rings

Labrinth groove ⅟32" wide
⅟64" deep
Details of piston valve head

FIG. 37

'Solid' piston valve. Poor passage layout
FIG. 38

makers as Stanley, White and Doble should be sufficient guarantee of its merits. In this connection, I remember some time ago in the course of a controversy on the subject one gentleman spoke highly of rusty nails!

In my opinion slide valves for cast iron cylinders should be themselves of cast iron particularly for superheated steam. For G.M. cylinders I favour a built-up slide valve with a stainless steel working face. Too much trouble cannot be taken to ensure dimensional accuracy of the working face and exhaust cavity of the slide valve, for on it depends the accuracy of the steam distribution (always assuming of course that your valve gear is right!).

Lagging is referred to elsewhere, but it is worthwhile emphasising here that it should always be applied to cylinders and done as thoroughly as possible, and that includes the end covers, as well as cylinder body, steam chest and steam chest cover.

PISTON VALVES AND BALANCED SLIDE VALVES

As previously mentioned piston valves are not recommended, other than for the H.P. valve of a compound or triple expansion engine, unless they can be made large enough to be fitted with rings, say, $\frac{3}{4}$ in. diameter or larger. When they are used, they should in all normal circumstances be of the " inside admission " type.

They should always be made with extended piston valve chambers as shown in Fig. 36 which allows of short straight steam passages. On no account follow the antediluvian " design " shown in Fig. 38 which has been largely applied to model locomotives in the past, it is thoroughly inefficient and possesses no obvious merits whatsoever. It not only involves unnecessarily indirect steam (and exhaust) passages but it considerably reduces the size of the live steam space, which is already small enough in all conscience. This form has been outmoded and discarded in full size practice for many years and there is no more sense in perpetuating it than in perpetuating the stone axe or the flint knife!

The centre line of the valve chamber should be kept as close to the centre line of the cylinder as constructional considerations will allow. Piston valve chambers should always be fitted with liners, and the bore of the liners should in no case be less than half the cylinder bore, preferably rather more. Various methods of finishing the liner bore after forcing into the housing have been advocated, the one I have found best is to do this with an adjustable reamer taking only the lightest possible cuts. Before forcing the liner into place coat its exterior surfaces where they are in contact with its housing with a thin freshly mixed coating of red lead and linseed oil. Piston valve liners should be of similar material to the cylinder body.

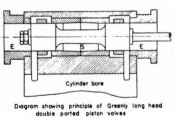

Diagram showing principle of Greenly long head double ported piston valves

FIG. 39

The long headed double ported valve, Fig. 39, introduced many years ago by Hy Greenly has many advocates; it undoubtedly has certain advantages, but in my personal opinion these are outweighed by the considerably increased clearance volumes entailed and by the much less direct admission. Fig. 37 shows in detail a piston valve. Firstly it should be noted that it is the *edges of the rings* which control the admission and exhaust. The arrangement of two spring rings, with a solid floating separator ring between them is one I have found to work well in practice in sizes from $\frac{3}{4}$ in. diameter up to $2\frac{1}{2}$ in.

Where the piston valve is large enough the " Clupet " double

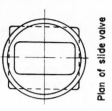

Plan of slide valve

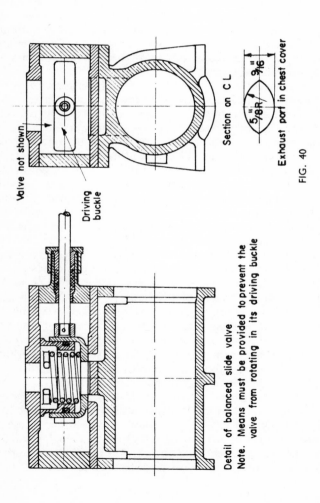

Valve not shown

Driving buckle

Section on C L

Exhaust port in chest cover

$5\frac{7}{8}''R$ $9\frac{1}{16}''$

FIG. 40

Detail of balanced slide valve
Note. Means must be provided to prevent the valve from rotating in its driving buckle

key ring is ideal, I believe that they can be obtained as small as ⅞ in. diameter.   It is essential to locate the spring rings positively so that they cannot turn and in such a manner that the slit always travels over a " bridge " between the port openings in the liner, unless this is done there is a risk of the split ends catching in the ports with disastrous results.   It follows that the piston valve spool must also be prevented from rotating on the valve spindle, otherwise there would be no point in pegging the rings.   Apart from being restrained from rotating the spool should be free to float on the valve spindle, of course without any end shake.   Some people advocate making the ports rather longer than normal requirements would dictate, but not opening them fully, claiming that this tends to give freer ingress and egress to the steam, but I am inclined to think that this is of doubtful value.   It would require a considerable number of carefully controlled tests to obtain reliable data, and in any case there is probably very little in it.

An alternative to the piston valve which has some of its advantages and few of its disabilities, is the balanced slide valve.

This, curiously enough, has been almost entirely neglected in model practice, and in fact many model engineers are not familiar with it.   Its virtues are such as to make it worthy of a full description.   Fig. 40 shows in detail a valve of this description, well adapted to model work and perfectly straightforward from the constructional point of view for any model engineer of average skill.   A study of the drawing will make clear its principle.   Particular attention should be directed to the beautifully free path it provides for the exhaust, which is discharged straight through its open back, there being no exhaust port at all in the port face.   There are, by the way, a number of differing schemes to accomplish the balancing, this one which is probably the best adapted for amateur construction and for small sizes is the Adams, invented many years ago by a famous locomotive superintendent of that name.   The balancing piston is kept in contact with the steam chest cover by a light coil spring and this piston must be a really accurate fit in the valve body.   In my experience, if this part of the job is accurately carried out, simple labyrinth grooves in the piston will ensure steamtight working, but if anyone is doubtful about this a groove can be cut in it to accommodate a length of soft graphited asbestos packing.

Another essential is that the face of the steam chest cover must be perfectly parallel, in both planes, with the port face, but this is not a matter which is likely to trouble any reasonably competent mechanic.   This form of valve is not of course completely balanced, but it takes a very great deal less driving than does a normal unbalanced slide valve, with consequent benefits to the life of the valve gear. It has the advantage too that it takes up its own wear. Where this type of valve is used, it is recommended that joints between steam chest and cylinder body and steam chest and cover should be made with thin copper sheet as already referred to in this chapter. So far as valve events are concerned, these are exactly as for a normal unbalanced slide valve. Rather more height is required in the steam chest than is perhaps normal but this is advantageous inasmuch as increasing the effective volume, as previously mentioned, a desirable feature.

Concluding this chapter it may again be emphasised that the cylinder(s) is the heart of the engine and only the very best workmanship of which you are capable is good enough. A little extra time and care spent on making these vital components will pay for itself many times over. Finally, don't forget that the best of cylinders requires regular and adequate lubrication with high-grade cylinder oil if it is to function efficiently. So far as actual construction is concerned, it is very little more trouble to follow correct principles throughout, than it is to work to crude forms of design which can only result in an avoidable loss of efficiency and which will to a large extent cancel out the advantages accruing from even the very best of workmanship.

SAFE LOADS. B.A. STEEL SCREWS
Based on stress of 8,000 lb. per sq. in. of Core Area

SIZE No. B.A.	DIA. OVER THREAD INS.	CORE AREA SQ. INS.	SAFE LOAD LBS.
16	·031	·00039	3·1
14	·039	·00064	5·1
12	·051	·00113	9·0
11	·059	·00155	12·4
10	·067	·00196	15·7
9	·075	·00250	20·0
8	·087	·00345	27·6
7	·098	·00453	36·2
6	·110	·00566	45·5
5	·126	·00757	60·5
4	·142	·00962	77·0
3	·161	·0126	100
2	·185	·0172	137
1	·209	·0218	174
0	·236	·0282	255

RECOMMENDED BOLT HEAD AND NUT PROPORTIONS
Based on Thread diameter

Hexagons. Width across flats = Diameter × 1·75 to nearest Std.
Height of Bolt Heads = Diameter × ·875
,, ,, Std. Nuts = Diameter
,, ,, Nuts Heavy Loading = Diameter × 1·25 to 1·5
,, ,, Lock Nuts = Diameter × ·625
Where extra strength is required from ⅛ in. diameter upwards use " M.E." 40 t.p.i. up to ⅜ in. and above this standard brass pipe 26 t.p.i. all diameters.

CHAPTER 14

CONDENSING

IN FULL size practice condensers have been fitted to a large proportion of stationary engines, particularly of the larger types, and universally to marine engines required to propel vessels operating on salt water. Even for quite small launch engines to operate on rivers and lakes, condensing apparatus was frequently fitted in order to improve the thermal efficiency of the plant.

Condensers are applied for two reasons.

(a) To increase efficiency, i.e. to get more work from a given amount of fuel, or alternatively to get a given amount of work from a reduced consumption of coal.

(b) To economise in the use of water where it is in short supply.

Incidentally, both these factors apply to marine work, and in not a few cases to land work too.

Without delving into thermo-dynamics, the reasons for increased thermal efficiency achieved by condensing, are (a) the increased range of temperature between admission and rejection of the steam used in the cylinder (i.e. the extraction from the steam of an increased proportion of its energy) and (b) the reduction in back pressure on the exhaust side of the piston, due to exhausting into a more or less perfect vacuum (usually about 26 in. to 28 in. of mercury) which results in a higher mean effective pressure, and hence in a greater horse power.

Regarding water conservation, the outstanding example is to be found in marine work. In the early days of steam ships the boilers were fed with salt water and this of course entailed the rapid concentration of salts in the boilers, in turn necessitating their frequent blowing-down to clear out the accumulated deposits and supersaturated water. Naturally this was very wasteful of heat and it also severely limited the pressure at which the boilers could be worked. The introduction of the surface condenser wrought a revolution in economy and enabled pressures to be raised from 15-25 lb. to 60-80-100 lb. and so on, until today we are frequently working at pressures approaching 1,000 lb. per sq. in. This rise in pressure in turn made possible the introduction of the compound, triple and quadruple expansion engine.

There are three main systems of condensing.

(1) The oldest, *Jet Condensing*, dating from the times of Savery and Newcomen, when it was actually carried out in the engine cylinder itself, a most dreadfully wasteful proceeding. James Watt invented the separate condenser, thereby at one stroke rendering the older system completely obsolete.

In jet condensing, the steam is brought into direct contact with the cooling water and mixes with it. This was the system applied to marine engines in the days when salt water was used in the boilers and it was also the system most generally used in land work. Actually, all the early steam engines, incluyding Watt's, relied on the pressure of the atmosphere to produce their power, the steam being supplied at atmospheric pressure and by its condensation providing a simple means of creating a more or less complete vacuum below the piston.

To Murdoch belongs the credit for introducing the engine operated directly by steam at a pressure above that of the atmosphere. In passing, Watt took a very dim view of this idea, just an example of how the greatest engineers can have their blind spots and prejudices.

(2) *Surface Condensing*. In this form, the steam to be condensed does *not* come into contact with the cooling water. The usual arrangement is to have a closed vessel through which pass a large number of small tubes, and through which tubes cold water is circulated, the steam being led into the top of the closed vessel, condensing on the tubes and the resulting condensate extracted from the bottom of the vessel. The vessel must be capable of withstanding an *external* pressure of at least 15 lb. per sq. in.

Occasionally in Admiralty practice, the arrangement was reversed, the water being circulated in the vessel, and the steam being passed through the tubes, but in the Merchant Marine, the first mentioned arrangement was almost always used.

(3) *Evaporative Condensing*. This is itself a form of surface condensing, in which the steam to be condensed is passed through a battery of tubes, usually situated in the open air, over which streams of water are sprayed, some of the cooling effect is direct, but most of it due to part of the cooling water evaporating and in so doing taking up heat from the surface of the tubes and of course, their contents. Frequently this form of condenser was arranged over a large cooling pond, and the water pumped from this and sprayed over the battery of condenser tubes.

Of these we need only consider the first two, the evaporative condenser is not a good *working-model* proposition largely on account of its messiness, its chief virtue in full-size practice was economy in cooling water.

Before considering condensers in detail, the function of the air pump must be dealt with. To the uninitiated there is apt to be some misunderstanding as tᴏ the function of this vital component of the condensing plant, whether it be Jet, Surface or Evaporative. The air pump does *not* create the vacuum, that is done by the condensation of the steam. In boiler feed water there is always present a certain amount of air in solution, and when the water is boiled the air is driven out of solution and passes with the steam through the engine. Furthermore a certain amount of air is apt to leak through the piston rod gland on the exhaust stroke *into* the cylinder, where the pressure is now much below that of the atmosphere. (It is a curious thing, but it always seems much more difficult to make a gland " vacuum tight " than " pressure-tight ", don't ask me why!) Now air, under the conditions existing in a condenser, cannot be itself condensed, and if it were allowed to accumulate would rapidly fill up the condenser, greatly to the detriment of its efficiency; hence the air pump. The air pump, as its title denotes, not only clears out this unwanted air, but also the condensed steam which it delivers as water to the " hot-well " in the form of a tank with a vent pipe open to atmosphere, from which the feed pumps draw their supply.

In one form or another an air pump is an essential component of any condensing plant.

Now to consider in detail the apparatus required in condensing systems.

Fig. 41 shows a jet condenser and it will be seen that it is a comparatively simple piece of apparatus. This form was one very largely used with horizontal engines and was most frequently placed in line with and behind the cylinder, the low-pressure cylinder in a compound or triple expansion engine, the air-pump being driven by the piston tail rod, and of course having the same stroke as the piston.

The body of the condenser could be made as a casting, but it would require some fairly elaborate pattern and corebox making and would be expensive to mould. All things considered it would probably be best to fabricate it (unless you are going in for quantity production!) As for " one-off " you could probably do this just about as quickly as you could make the necessary patterns and coreboxes.

Considering the figure the chamber C is the actual condenser, S being the steam inlet connection and $S.P.$ the spray pipe through which the condensing water is delivered. Chamber P is the pump chamber and chamber D the delivery chamber, connected to the hot well by the pipe $D1$. The inlet or suction valves $S.V.$ provide communication between the chamber C and opposite ends of cham-

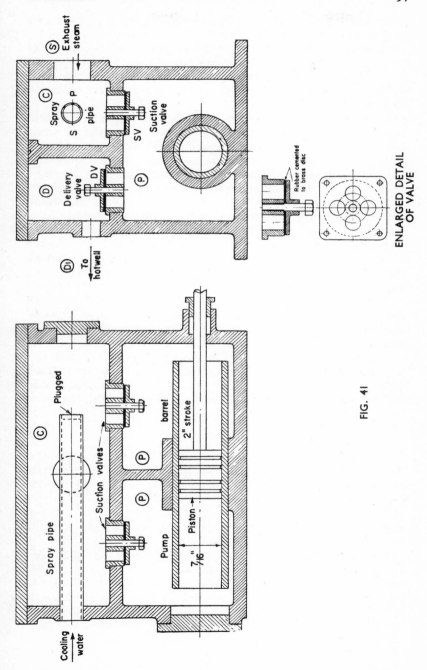

ENLARGED DETAIL OF VALVE

FIG. 41

ber *P*, whilst similar delivery valves *D.V.* connect the opposite ends of chamber *P* with chamber *D*.

In working, the incoming steam meets the spray of cold water from *S.P.* and is immediately condensed, the cooling water condensed steam and air are drawn through the suction valves by the pump and delivered through the delivery valves to chamber *D* and thence to the hot well.

It will be seen that the whole thing is quite simple both in construction and in operation and there is very little that can go wrong or cause trouble so long as the valves are tight and the pump piston a good fit. The apparatus is compact and self-contained, the only addition required is a small pump to supply the water to the spray, unless a source of supply under a few pounds pressure is available.

In most cases in model work, the domestic water supply would conveniently fill this requirement. In the small sizes likely to be of interest to model engineers, the valves may best be made from brass discs, faced with rubber, which can be stuck to them with one of the many modern adhesives now available, as no very high temperatures are in question. The pump plunger is probably best made without any form of packing, it should be a really close fit in the barrel with two to four shallow labyrinth grooves cut on its cylindrical surface. Air pump sizes are dealt with later. The condenser shown in the drawing is suitable for a cylinder of 1¼ in. bore by 2 in. stroke. Air pumps may be single-acting or double-acting.

For model jet condensers the double-acting type is to be preferred, as in the single-acting type there is usually a valve in the piston itself, which is not a very satisfactory proposition in small sizes. Whilst the fitting of a vacuum gauge to indicate the vacuum existing in the

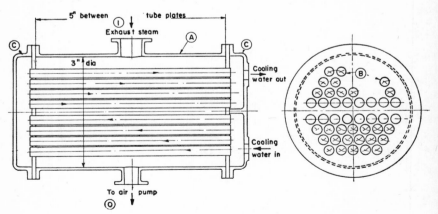

FIG. 42

condenser is not necessary, it is certainly more in accordance with full size practice to fit one, besides which it is interesting to watch, and it is helpful to know just how much (or little!) vacuum you are getting.

Turning now to the Surface Condenser, this is considerably more complicated. The reason for its universal use in modern marine practice is to be found in the fact that it keeps the cooling water and condensate entirely separate, the sea provides unlimited quantities of cooling water which of course is salt, whilst the condenser provides what is practically pure distilled water for the boilers. Cylinder lubrication in marine work is kept to a practical minimum in order to minimise as much as possible the contamination of the feed-water with oil, which is very bad indeed for boilers and can rapidly lead to overheating of plates and tubes if in appreciable quantities.

Fig. 42 shows diagrammatically the layout of a surface condenser of medium size. A is the condenser body, B are the circulating tubes through which the cooling water is pumped, $C.C.$ are the end chambers for providing access for the cooling water to the tubes and collecting it after it has done its work, as shown here it passes in through the lower bank of tubes, and out through the upper bank. Steam inlet is at I and outlet for condensate and air at O.

It will be noted that the hottest steam meets the warmer upper tubes first and the colder lower ones last, on the contra-flow principle which is always recognized as the most effective and efficient method to apply to heat transference apparatus. Air pumps for surface condensers are usually of the single-acting type in marine work (modern) always vertical and usually driven at a reduced stroke by rocker arms off the L.P. Crosshead gudgeon pin.

Usually too the circulating pump, feed pump and bilge pump are incorporated with the air pump in a single unit, all driven off the same beam. In Naval vessels, it was usual practice to provide separate engines to operate these pumps but pumps driven by the main engines were the general rule in the Merchant Marine. Reverting for a moment to the condenser itself, one of the most troublesome things about its construction is to find a satisfactory method of fitting the tubes in such a manner that whilst being free to expand and move slightly endways (strictly speaking it is the body which expands and moves over the tubes) they shall remain quite vacuum tight. It will be appreciated that any leakage of sea water into the condenser body would be very bad indeed for the boilers. Fig. 43 shows two methods of accomplishing this, which we can call A ancient and B modern.

In my young days I must have fitted some thousands of ferrules

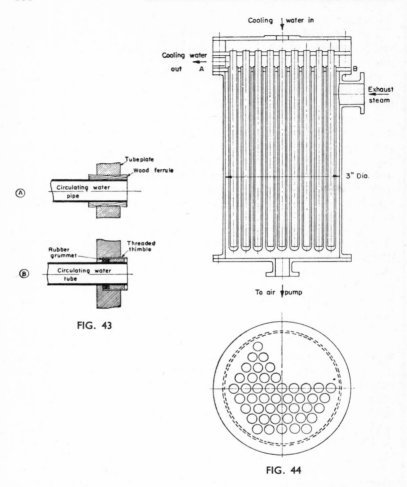

FIG. 43

FIG. 44

to condenser tubes, and to add insult to injury, we had to make the
grommets or packings ourselves from spun yarn and tallow, (modern
practice uses packings of special rubber or some synthetic substitute)
this was a filthy job, your clothes got impregnated with the tallow
and so did your skin, and you were not fit to move in civilized
society for days! In model work, neither method is satisfactory, or in
fact really practicable, and in my opinion the only form of construction which will give good results is to allow a good margin of
space between the outer row of tubes and the condenser body, use
as thin tubeplates as are safe and solder the tubes in place. This

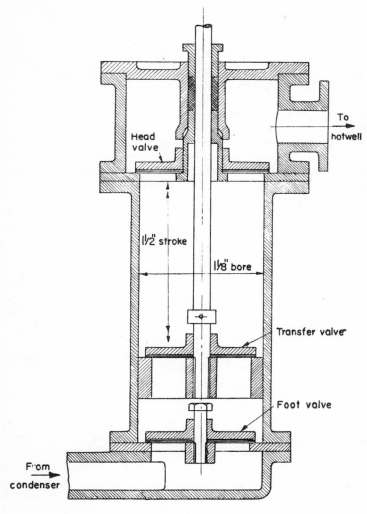

FIG. 45

allows the tubeplates themselves to take up the small degree of movement involved. Alternatively the tubes might be expanded and beaded, but I think, taken all round, soft soldering is the safest proposition.

The amount of tube surface required for a given duty is dealt with later.

From the model engineer's point of view the return tube condenser Fig. 44 has many advantages and entirely eliminates expansion troubles, as the tubes are fixed at one end only. This form of condenser was largely used by Savery's, who as I have remarked elsewhere, built what were probably the most efficient small- and medium-sized launch engines, compounds and triples, ever made anywhere in the world. It will be seen that the cooling water flows down the inner tube and up the outer concentric tube, the steam being brought in at the top, where the cooling water is warmest, and the outlet being at the bottom. It is worth mentioning in passing that this form of construction is equally applicable to exhaust feed-water heaters and gives excellent results. As shown the condenser is arranged vertically, but it can equally well be made horizontal if that is more convenient. Where an efficient working model is required, it is my opinion that this form of condenser is much to be preferred.

Regarding air pumps for surface condensers, these as already stated are usually of the single-acting vertical type. Fig. 45 shows a typical air pump having foot valves, transfer valves in the piston and head or delivery valves, quite a complicated job to produce satisfactorily in model form and not to be recommended for conditions where an efficient *working* model is the primary consideration. Fig. 46 shows the " Edwards " air pump which has largely displaced the form shown in Fig. 45. As will be seen there are no foot valves and no transfer valves either, only head valves, which are at all times readily accessible without having to dismantle the whole pump. The pump works thus:

As the piston descends it strikes the water which has flowed into the conical base from the condenser and via the curved annulus projects it silently and without shock through the row of ports uncovered by the piston; the piston ascends driving the air and water through the head valves, from whence it flows to the hot well. The " Edwards " pump is to be strongly recommended for working model purposes, the one shown in Fig. 46 is suitable for an engine, compound or triple, having an L.P. cylinder $2\frac{1}{2}$ in. bore, $1\frac{3}{4}$ in. stroke. It will be appreciated that the jet condenser air pump has to deal not only with the air and condensate, but with the spray water used to effect condensation, but the surface condenser air

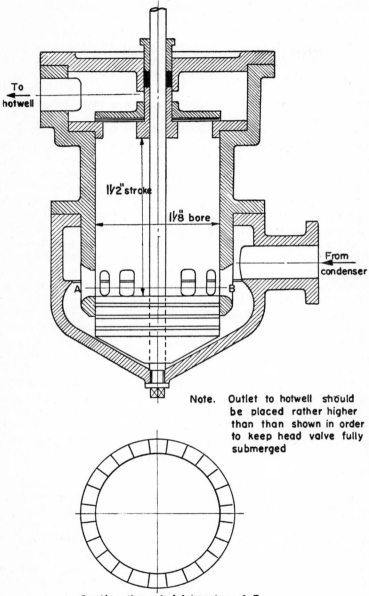

To
hotwell

1½" stroke

1⅛" bore

From
condenser

A   B

Note. Outlet to hotwell should
       be placed rather higher
       than than shown in order
       to keep head valve fully
       submerged

Section through inlet ports on A-B

FIG. 46

pump has only to deal with air and condensate, the cooling water being in an entirely separate circulatory system.

The size of air pumps is next to be considered. For jet condensers the air pump should have a swept capacity of from one-fifth to one-sixth of that of the cylinder it serves when single acting, (that is reckoning the swept capacity of a single stroke), and half this figure when double-acting. For model work the larger figure is advisable. These figures of course assume that the pump is driven at engine speed.

For surface condensers the air pump should be one-tenth to one-fifth the capacity of the cylinder (the L.P. cylinder in compound or triple expansion engines) if single-acting and half this if double-acting. For model purposes a single-acting " Edwards " type pump of about one-sixth cylinder capacity is recommended.

With cooling water at around 55 deg. F. an allowance for a jet condenser of about 20-25 lb. of water per pound of steam to be condensed will be about right.

The diameter of the injection pipe may be around one-twelfth of that of the cylinder for slow speed engines and one-seventh for high speed engines.

About the same amount of cooling water is required for a surface condenser as for a jet condenser, but it is safer to allow 30-35 lb. per pound of steam to be condensed.

When considering the area of tube surface required in a surface condenser it is fairly safe to make it equal to the area of heating surface of the boiler, assuming that cooling water is available at 50-55 deg. F.

All these figures are empirical, but under average conditions will be found to work out satisfactorily. Strictly speaking each case should be worked out individually taking into account all the prevailing conditions, but not all model engineers are sufficiently *au fait* with the theory of heat to do this and the information given can be relied upon to give satisfactory results under all average conditions.

Where possible the speed of the piston of the air pump should not exceed 5 to 6 feet per second, though in certain cases of high speed launch engines this speed has often been greatly exceeded. Air pumps should always have the very best possible work put into their " internals ", a truly bored barrel, with the bore absolutely parallel throughout and a good surface finish, should have a really accurately fitting piston and the only form of " packing " should be narrow and shallow square bottomed grooves cut in the cylindrical surface of the piston.

There is another variety of condenser which is of interest to model engineers who want simplicity combined with efficiency, that is the ejector condenser. This requires for its operation a constant supply of water at a reasonable pressure, say 20 lb. per sq. in. or over, and here again the domestic mains supply is ideal. The drawback to this form of condenser, from the model engineer's standpoint is that as it has no moving parts there is nothing to be seen when it is in operation. Fig. 47 shows an ejector condenser and it will at once be appreciated what an extremely simple piece of apparatus it is; it requires no air pump, as the ejector action of the water jet

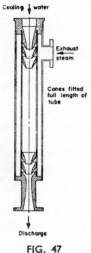

Cooling water

Exhaust steam

Cones fitted full length of tube

Discharge

FIG. 47

entrains the air along with the condensate and withdraws it from the system.

The late Hy Greenly embodied a condenser of this type, particulars of which are to be found in *Model Engineering* written by him and first published by Cassell's in 1915, since when it has run through many editions. In this particular case the condenser was used in conjunction with an automatic small power steam plant embodying an enclosed single-acting compound engine and a flash boiler for solid fuel firing.

The ejector condenser is a very simple one with which to carry out experiments and has much to recommend it. This applies particularly to those who are desirous of knowing what are the effects of adding a condenser to an existing engine.

For those who want to go more thoroughly into the theory and practice of condensing, ample information is to be found in engineering text books, more particularly those published between 1880 and 1910. Hutton's *Practical Engineers Handbook* which could be found in any decent Reference Library contains a great deal of highly practical information on the subject. In conclusion, the addition of condensing apparatus to a model will improve its efficiency (always providing it is properly carried out), add to its interest and is in every way worthwhile for the keen model enthusiast.

CHAPTER 15

REVERSING GEARS

PROBABLY MORE ink has been spilt, more wordy arguments propounded and more patents developed on the subject of steam engine valve gears than on almost any other phase of mechanical engineering with the possible exception of boilers.

There is an enormous (and vastly interesting) bibliography on steam engine valve gears, and the patent files of more than 120 years are cluttered up with largely forgotten specifications of valve gears which their inventors fondly hoped would revolutionise the industry (which by and large they signally failed to do).

Obviously this is not the place to attempt to deal in detail with this vast subject and I propose to refer quite briefly to a few reversing valve gears only which have proved their value over many years. It is a salutary thought that the two gears used by probably over 90 per cent. of British locomotives today were both invented over 100 years ago !

The action of the slide valve and eccentric has already been explained and I suggest that at this stage anyone not thoroughly familiar with this matter should re-read this portion. I propose to deal only with five reversing gears, all of which are of practical interest and use to the model steam engine enthusiast and all of which can be applied equally well to stationary engines, marine engines, or locomotives.

These are the slip eccentric; Stephenson's (more correctly Howe's) link motion; Walschaerts radial gear; Hackworth's gear, and Joy's gear. These are set out in the order in which they were invented. As a matter of interest I have records of well over 120 different valve gears intended for operating an ordinary piston or slide valve.

The slip eccentric, Fig. 48, appeared in the 1820's and so far as I can find nobody knows who invented it, it was used on many of the earliest steam locomotives.

" Stephenson's " gear, Fig. 48, was invented by a man named Howe, a foreman in Robert Stephenson & Sons' Forth Street Works, at Newcastle in 1842; I believe that where it can be made mechanically satisfactory, that it is still the best valve gear for a locomotive,

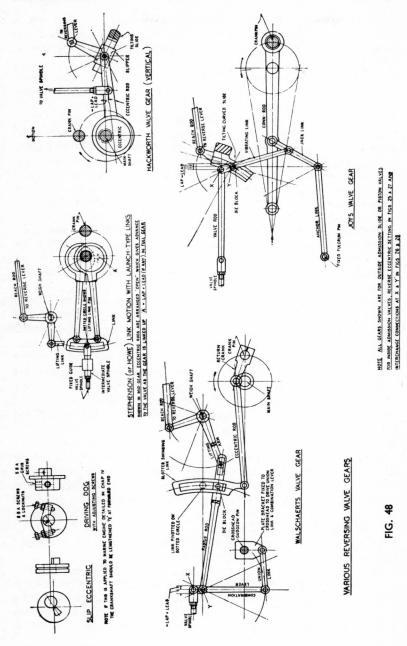

HACKWORTH VALVE GEAR (VERTICAL)

JOY'S VALVE GEAR

STEPHENSON (or HOWE) LINK MOTION WITH LAUNCH-TYPE LINKS

SHOWN IN MID-GEAR, ECCENTRIC RODS ARE ARRANGED 'OPEN' WHICH GIVES ADVANCE TO THE VALVE AS THE GEAR IS LINKED UP   A = LAP + LEAD (IF ANY) IN FULL GEAR

WALSCHAERTS VALVE GEAR

SLIP ECCENTRIC

DRIVING DOG
WITH ADJUSTING SCREWS

NOTE IF THIS IS APPLIED TO MARINE ENGINE DETAILED IN CHAP IV THE CRANKSHAFT SHOULD BE LENGTHENED 'Z' AT FORWARD END

NOTE ALL GEARS SHOWN ARE FOR OUTSIDE ADMISSION SLIDE OR PISTON VALVES FOR INSIDE ADMISSION VALVES, REVERSE ECCENTRIC SETTING IN FIGS 25 & 27 AND INTERCHANGE CONNECTIONS AT X & Y IN FIGS 26 & 28

VARIOUS REVERSING VALVE GEARS

FIG. 48

full size or model.   Before proceeding to describe any of the gears it would be well to stress two points about which there is much misunderstanding and on which many grossly misleading statements have been made.

Firstly there is no such thing as the " best " valve gear; many things will help to decide which valve gear to use and given sound design and good workmanship, the difference in performance to be expected from fitting in succession, say, Stephenson's, Walschaerts, Hackworths', or Joy's valve gear will be very small indeed. Secondly, a lot of specious nonsense has been talked about certain valve gears " whipping the valve open " (or shut); they don't ! Broadly speaking the motion imparted to the valve by any normal type of valve gear is harmonic, and for *any particular setting* could be very closely matched indeed by a simple eccentric of suitable proportions and setting.

Walschaerts gear, Fig. 48, was invented a year after Stephenson's by a man named Egide Walschaerts, a foreman in the Belgian State Railway shops.

So far as I know neither the Stephenson (Howe) gear nor the Walschaerts gear were ever patented.

Hackworth's gear, Fig. 48, was invented and patented in 1859 by John (not Timothy) Hackworth and was the forerunner and " father " of a number of similar gears, including Joy's, many of which, including Hackworth's own, still survive in modern practice.

Joy's gear, Fig. 48, was invented by David Joy and patented around 1877-8 and it has been extensively used in both locomotive and marine practice, over 3,000 British locomotives having been fitted with it.   Incidentally, the late David Joy probably was one of the few inventors of valve gear to make a substantial income from his invention for a long period.

The slip eccentric is the simplest of all reversing gears, but suffers from the disadvantage that it cannot be directly reversed. To get over this, early steam engines fitted with it were provided with an arrangement by which the eccentric could temporarily be disengaged from the valve and the latter operated by hand until the engine was moving in the required direction when the eccentric rod was hooked up with the valve again.

Fig. 48 shows details of a slip eccentric suitable for the single cylinder marine engine described in Chapter 4, Fig. 12.

It has been stated on numerous occasions in the model engineering press, that the slip eccentric is the only reversing valve gear which gives a perfectly even series of valve events at each end of the cylinder and similar events in either forward or reverse gear.   This is *not true*.   The angularities of both connecting-rod and valve-rod

make this impossible, the only conditions under which these statements could hold good would be in a case where both piston rod
and valve rod were operated by a " scotch " or slipper crank arrangement, which, of course, gives the same effect as connecting and valve
rods of infinite length. So long as connecting rod and valve rod
are of reasonable lengths proportionate to the crank and eccentric
throws, the errors introduced are slight and of no matter, but
emphatically the statement quoted is *not* correct as, though contrary
to another commonly stated fallacy, Nature *can* be " scaled " and
is being " scaled " every day in research laboratories and experimental shops the world over, Nature's laws, which include those of
geometry, cannot be evaded, even by the greatest genius yet born,
and in that same connection a knowledge of elementary geometry
is a help in designing valve gears, the functioning of which are
governed almost entirely by geometrical principles.

Valve gear models are of the utmost value in trying out the effects
of minor adjustments or modifications *after* you have properly laid
out your gear in the first place. People who rely on " trial and
error " methods will meet with a lot of trials and make a lot of
errors.

In making slip eccentric gear, the eccentric bore should be an
easy turning fit on the shaft, but on no account should it be loose
or sloppy. By fitting screws, as shown in Fig. 48, to the faces of
the driving block, it is possible to make adjustments to the eccentric
setting, and try out in running the effect of differing degrees of
" advance." Webb's later three-cylinder compounds on the old
L.N.W.R. all had slip eccentrics to drive the L.P. valve (inside the
frames). This was simple and cheap and generally satisfactory in
working, but occasionally led at starting to the front pair of wheels
running one way whilst the rear pair ran the other, not, perhaps,
what one would describe as an altogether desirable state of affairs
or one likely to lead to a quick get-away. (The L.P cylinder drove
the front driving wheel crank axle and the H.P. cylinders the rear
driving wheels, and the wheels were *not* coupled.)

Fig. 48 shows a Stephenson link motion valve gear. Though simple
in general principles I have always regarded this gear as one which
requires a great deal of understanding if the best is to be got out of
it. In one of the finest series of articles ever to be published in
the *Model Engineer* in the latter half of 1937, the late G. S.
Willoughby dealt fully with this gear in its up-to-date form, as
applied to model locomotives, and to those who wish to go more
deeply into the subject I most strongly recommend that they should
read this outstanding series.

The late G. S. Willoughby was a sound practical engineer with a real insight into and knowledge of the principles involved in steam engine design and construction.

Points to watch in layout are to allow sufficient length of slot in the curved link to provide for what is usually called " die slip," but is actually " link slip."

Another point is to ensure that the lifting link or drag link (or links, they are frequently double, one each side the link) is so pivoted to the operating lever or arm that when the link is in mid position with the crank on either dead centre it lies parallel with a line tangential to the centre of the link arc. (See sketch A.)

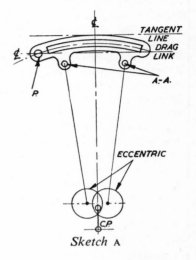

Sketch A

This is, of course, not absolutely hard and fast, but approximate only, the object being that the point P shall be displaced as little as possible sideways of the vertical centre line as the end of the link moves up and down. The longer the drag link can be made the better. The centres of the holes A, A should be kept as close to the centre line of the slot as is practicable.

There are two other well-known forms of double eccentric valve gear, the " Gooch " in which the link is slung from a fixed point to a pivot about the centre of its slot, and the end of the valve rod moved up or down in the slot, the curve of the link being *convex* to the crankshaft, whereas that of the Stephenson gear is concave. This was invented by John Viret Gooch, the brother of the better known Sir Daniel Gooch, about 1843.

The other gear is the Allan, invented by Alexander Allan of the Crewe works some years later (1859). In this gear a *straight* slotted link is used and both link and valve rod are moved (in opposite directions) to reverse or link-up.

Both these gears were extensively used in the early days of locomotives but both are now no longer in vogue. Details can be found in any good treatise on the steam engine published prior to 1900.

Fig. 48 shows the Walschaerts which is an excellent gear and today is probably fitted to more locomotives than all the other gears put together.

In principle it is quite simple and it has the great advantage that

it automatically divides into two parts, one of which, the union
link and combination lever, supplies the motion for lap and lead
whilst the other, return crank or eccentric, eccentric rod, slotted
link, and valve rod or radius rod provide the main motion and enable
the engine to be reversed or the point of cut-off varied. It should
be appreciated that a return crank is only a specialised form of
eccentric (or vice versa, if you prefer it) but it should also be stressed
that whilst a return crank has certain advantages (reduction of
friction and total weight are the two most important ones) it also
has drawbacks. It calls for great accuracy in both making and
setting, and unless it is correctly laid out and made, it will be impossible to set it correctly as, unlike the eccentric, it is not mounted
upon the crankshaft, but on the crankpin; it is in effect a compound
eccentric and whereas a simple eccentric provided its throw is correct
can be angularly adjusted around the crankshaft to obtain correct
setting, this cannot be done with a return crank, as so doing at
the same time alters its total travel, it *must* be dimensionally correct
to enable it to be set correctly.

The amount of tilt of the slotted link on either side of its neutral
position, should not exceed 30 degrees. As with Stephenson, Gooch,
and Allan gears the design and layout of the reversing arrangements
is of the utmost importance, and unless correctly carried out excessive die slip will take place (and in Walschaerts gear it *is* die slip
and not link slip).

The aim should be so to lay out the lifting gear that the die-
block moves as little as possible in the link; the type of lifting gear
shown in Fig. 48 is quite the best geometrically as well as mechanically speaking where it can be worked in. Where an ordinary
lifting link has to be applied to the radius
rod it is an advantage (*a*) to make the link
as long as practicable and (*b*) to anchor it
to the radius rod *beyond* the slotted link
where this can be done. Where it cannot
be done then it should be connected to the
radius rod as close to the die block as possible; it is quite common to see lifting
links made as sketch B to help in this
direction.

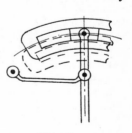

Sketch B

Finally, with regard to Walschaerts
gear, avoid so far as possible off-sets in the motion, aim to keep
return crankpin swinging slotted link, radius rod and combination
lever as nearly as possible in the same plane as the centre line of
the valve spindle.

Offset and dog-legged rods and links may " work," they are,

nevertheless, rank bad engineering practice as well as theoretically all wrong. Of course, the same principles apply to all other forms of valve gear.

Hackworth's gear, shown in Fig. 48, is the simplest of all the reversing gears which can be controlled by lever or screw, and it gives quite a good steam distribution when carefully laid out and made. It suffers from an inherent angularity error due to the finite length of the eccentric rod, which cannot be corrected, but this is of no serious moment. It has found its greatest field of use in marine work, particularly in the smaller sizes of screw engines.

The tilt of the reversing slide should not exceed 30 deg. each side of the mid-gear position.

Fig. 48 shows Joy's gear and a little study will show its affinities with the Hackworth gear, in fact, except that Joy usually used a *curved* slide (he did on occasion use a straight slide too) the gears from the foot of the vibrating link in the one case and the eccentric strap in the other are identical, the basic differences are two, firstly Joy derives his motion for his vibrating link from the connecting rod thus abolishing the need for an eccentric or return crank and secondly his gear is so designed as to avoid the angularity error, present and unavoidable in the Hackworth gear.

There are sundry modifications of both Hackworth and Joy gears to meet special circumstances, but these are more appropriately dealt with in the specialised valve gear literature to be found in any good technical reference library.

With any of the radial valve gears, i.e., with gears such as the Walschaerts, Joy, Hackworth, Baker or Greenly, where the reversing gear can be moved over from forward to reverse with the engine on either dead centre, *without causing any movement of the valve*, there is only one possible setting of the valve which will give even leads at each end of the cylinder and nobody can do anything about it (short, of course, of altering the physical proportions of valve or valve gear).

Valve gears can undoubtedly be made to " work " by hit and miss trial and error methods, but I do suggest that some knowledge of what you should aim at on the one hand, and some knowledge of the geometrical laws governing the functioning of the apparatus you are setting out to design on the other, are likely to lead you to a sounder final result much more quickly and will enable you to avoid many trials, errors, and misses on the way !

Incidentally, the errors introduced by the use of straight, as opposed to curved slides have been exaggerated *ad nauseam* in the past, though strangely enough these strictures have been applied to Greenly's gear and not to Hackworth's. These are the facts:

a straight slide does introduce an error depending upon the relative length of the valve rod, but small in any case. By the use of a simple geometrical construction however, involving no additional parts or work, this error can be completely corrected. The curved slide gives correct timing in mid gear (where it is never used !) but introduces errors of port opening when tilted *for which there is no correction*. Statements that Greenly's corrected gear cannot be linked up have often been made (Greenly's corrected gear is a more compact form of Heywood's gear, itself a variant of Joy's), but these statements do not accord with facts. If the principles governing its action are understood and if properly designed, constructed and erected according to them, Greenly's gear will give an excellent distribution right up to mid gear in either direction. In this respect it is at least equal to Walschaerts, one of the best of the type. In fairness to the memory of a great model engineer the facts about his gear cannot be too strongly emphasised.

CHAPTER 16

LUBRICATION

THIS IS a subject, that so far as concerns models, receives far too little attention at least as regards lubrication of parts other than the valve chest and cylinder. This is all wrong, for on good lubrication, continuously applied, depends to quite a large extent not only the free running and efficient functioning of the model, but also its freedom from undue wear.

Lubrication of model engines falls under two distinct heads: (*a*) Lubrication of valve and cylinder unit, and (*b*) lubrication of main bearings, big and little ends of connecting rod, crosshead and guides, eccentric strap and valve rod joint, etc.: (*a*) can itself be subdivided into two methods, (1) the displacement lubricator, and (2) the positive mechanical lubricator; both of these in their turn can be further sub-divided, but we need not concern ourselves with this here. The displacement lubricator is essentially a very simple piece of apparatus though its functioning is apt to be somewhat puzzling to the beginner.

Sketch A shows the simplest form of displacement lubricator. *A* is a connection screwed directly into the steam chest, or the steam supply pipe close to the stop valve, and on the steam-chest side of it. *B* is the plug through which oil is introduced and is a pressure tight fit in the body *C*, whilst *D* is a drain valve, normally kept shut, but used to drain off the water which accumulates before re-filling with oil.

The action is as follows. First the lubricator is filled to just below the level of the hole in *A* (which hole incidentally requires to be kept very tiny indeed, for a small lubricator a No. 70 hole is ample). The plug *B* is replaced and tightened up. When steam is turned on, some of it enters through the hole in *A* and condenses, water being heavier than oil, it sinks to the bottom and so raises the level of the oil until it reaches the hole when some of it overflows

Sketch A

through the hole into the steampipe or steamchest where it is carried by the main steam supply over the valve and into the cylinder, and this process continues so long as there is any oil in the container C, and steam supply is maintained. The puzzling part is that whilst steam flows *into* C oil flows *out* by the same orifice, but puzzling or no, that is what *does* happen.

This simple type of lubricator in this actual form is quite satisfactory for small engines, but for larger sizes there are two most desirable improvements.

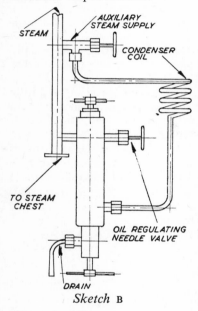

Sketch B

The first is to fit a regulating needle valve to the orifice, preferably with a long taper point so that a very fine adjustment can be made; the second is to arrange an independent steam supply with a regulating valve and a condenser, which usually takes the form of a coil in the steam supply pipe.

The accompanying sketch B shows the arrangement, and incidentally, a lubricator of this type can be seen on the picture of my rebuilt Stuart No. 1, which functions most satisfactorily. It may be worth while pointing out here that a displacement lubricator will *not* function when the engine is being run on compressed air, so if you are running a model on this power-source at an exhibition do not overlook this; make some other provision for keeping your valve and cylinder lubricated or you may have trouble.

This is an excellent and thoroughly reliable arrangement, quite suitable for all work other than such cases as involve maximum continuous power output combined with unusually high superheat, where a positive mechanical lubricator is strongly recommended.

I do not propose to detail a mechanical lubricator, as these have been detailed and re-detailed and detailed again in the *Model Engineer* over the last 25 years, until the details and descriptions must almost be able to find their own way into its pages; properly made they are thoroughly reliable instruments. It is always better to over lubricate a cylinder than to starve it, but there is neither sense nor use in overdoing it; so long as the exhaust steam carries over the least trace of oil, lubrication is sufficient, and anything more is wasteful and does no earthly good.

Always use a good grade of cylinder oil, and if using superheated steam, make sure the grade you choose is of " superheat " quality; there is no economy, in fact very much the reverse, in using cheap oil of any sort.

Where high performance over long periods combined with high superheat is in question, it is strongly recommended that a mechanical lubricator with two feeds be provided, one led to the steam supply just ahead of the steam chest and the other to the middle of the cylinder barrel, on or near the top centre line in the case of a horizontal engine.

Turning to general bearing and slide lubrication, one usually finds little or no provision made for it in most model engines other than a few casual oil holes or the odd oil cup.

Oil cups on *moving* parts, such as connecting rod big and little ends, eccentric straps, etc., should always have screwed caps, and it is not necessary to provide breather holes in the caps, the " working " of the bearings will allow air to get into the oil container to replace the oil. On the other hand static oil-cups may be left without caps, but should preferably have them, in which case a tiny air hole should be drilled in the cap. In all cases the oil holes should be quite small otherwise the oil drains away too quickly and is wasted.

In general the larger the content of the oil cup (without, of course, making it so large as to be out of proportion to the model) the better.

Where it can conveniently be used the wick feed type of lubricator is excellent. Sketch c herewith shows the principle which is extremely simple. A small pipe is fixed in the oil feed hole and stops

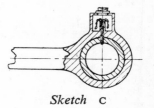

Sketch c

short of the lubricator top; into it are inserted two or three lengths of worsted, pushed well down, with their outer ends hanging over into the oil-well. Note particularly that the strands of worsted must on no account be *tightly* packed in the tube, otherwise the syphoning action will be prevented. With this type of lubricator it is well frequently to change the worsted, as in time it gets " gummy " and ceases to syphon over the oil.

Finally, good lubrication means ensuring an ample supply of oil applied to the correct spot, not a superfluity of oil slung all over the engine and surrounding district ! Use a medium machine oil for all except the smallest engines (other, of course, than for the cylinders); for very tiny engines, " 3 in 1 " is excellent.

CHAPTER 17

GOVERNORS

SOME FORM of governor is applied to the vast majority of Stationary engines, and for that matter to semi-portable, portable and traction engines and road locomotives. Exceptions are steam winches, some winding engines, reversible rolling mill engines etc.

Most steam engine governors depend on centrifugal force for their action, whether they be driven directly by the crankshaft or by belt and (or) gearing.

The oldest form of engine governor is Watt's shown in Fig. 49, usually driven by belt and bevel gearing. This type almost always operates a throttle valve in the steam supply line, usually of the Butterfly type; increasing speed of the engine causes the governor balls to move outwards and in so doing to lift the sliding collar attached to the lower links, and this in turn operates the bell crank and linkage and closes, or tends to close the throttle valve, see Fig. 50.

Broadly governors divide into two distinct types, or more accurately speaking, operate in two distinct manners. First and oldest method of governing was to throttle the steam supply, the second method is to vary the cut-off by the governor action, either by varying automatically the travel of the main eccentric, or, usually through some form of linkage, to vary the travel of a cut-off valve working on the back of the main slide valve. Figs. 50 and 52 show an arrangement of this type. The advantages of the separate cut-off valve are that the cut-off can be varied without in any way interfering with the exhaust cycle, i.e. timing of release and compression.

Shaft governors, i.e. governors mounted directly on the engine crankshaft if of the fly-ball type such as shown in Fig. 53, are almost always applied to a throttle valve, they are generally to be found on high speed engines, both enclosed and open.

The horizontal engine illustrated in Plates 5 and 6 is fitted with such a governor operating a butterfly throttle.

Plate 7 shows an engine fitted with a flywheel governor, which is of the auto-cut-off type and controls the travel of the main eccentric. In this case the effect is almost exactly the same as is attained by " linking up " a Stephenson, Gooch or Allan link motion.

117

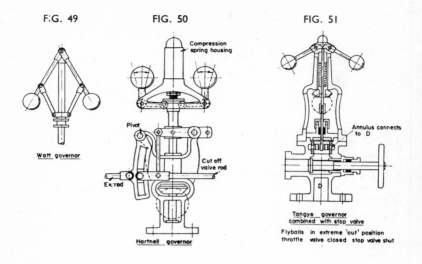

FIG. 49

Watt governor

FIG. 50

Compression spring housing

Pivot

Cut off valve rod

E L rod

Hartnell governor

FIG. 51

Annulus connects to D

D

Tangye governor combined with stop valve

Flyballs in extreme 'out' position throttle valve closed stop valve shut

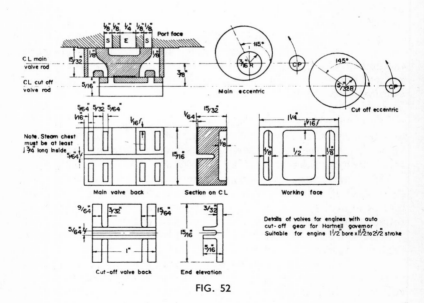

Port face

CL main valve rod

CL cut off valve rod

Main eccentric

Cut off eccentric

Note. Steam chest must be at least 1 3/4 long inside

Main valve back

Section on CL

Working face

Cut-off valve back

End elevation

Details of valves for engines with auto cut-off gear for Hartnell governor Suitable for engine 1 1/2 bore x 1 1/2 to 2 1/2 stroke

FIG. 52

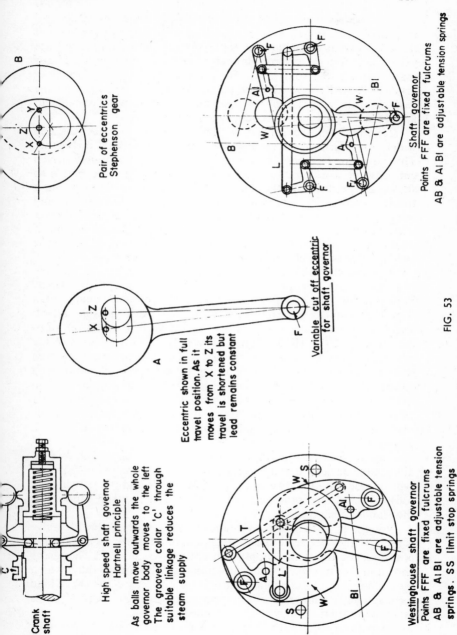

Pair of eccentrics
Stephenson gear

Eccentric shown in full
travel position. As it
moves from X to Z its
travel is shortened but
lead remains constant

Variable cut off eccentric
for shaft governor

Shaft governor
Points FFF are fixed fulcrums
AB & A1B1 are adjustable tension springs

High speed shaft governor
Hartnell principle

As balls move outwards the whole
governor body moves to the left
The grooved collar 'C' through
suitable linkage reduces the
steam supply

Crank
shaft

Westinghouse shaft governor
Points FFF are fixed fulcrums
AB & A1B1 are adjustable tension
springs. SS limit stop springs

FIG. 53

The Pickering governor was very largely used on small and medium-sized engines, always operating a balanced piston type of throttle valve or a double beat valve: usually the governor, throttle valve, and stop valve were made as a self-contained unit, and for many years it was sold in a wide variety of sizes as a proprietary article. Actually a Pickering-type governor is to be found on the vast majority of gramophone motors, and it is quite possible to adapt such a governor to model steam engine purposes.

Coming from the general to the particular, an excellent and widely used form of governor is the Hartnell illustrated in Fig. 50. This governor is generally arranged to operate a separately driven cut-off valve working on the back of the main slide valve, and is so shown in the drawing, though it is occasionally used to operate a throttle valve. It is a most attractive form of mechanism and fascinating to watch in operation. Fig. 52 gives details of main and cut-off valves with eccentric setting suitable for an engine of about $1\frac{1}{2}$ in. bore with a stroke of between $1\frac{1}{2}$ in. and $2\frac{1}{2}$ in., to the cut-off valve of which this type of governor is applicable.

Acknowledgement is here made to an article by the late Hy Muncaster which appeared in vol. XXVI (1912) of the *Model Engineer*, pp. 365 *et seq* which gives fairly complete details of a somewhat similar governor to the Hartnell with suitable cut-off and main valves etc. This was one of an excellent series on auto-cut-off gear in the same volume. The only minor criticisms of the governor shown in this article are that it is slightly more complicated than the Hartnell and has no means of adjusting the controlling spring; a minor item is that the footstep journal carrying the bottom of the governor spindle is flat bottomed, whereas it should preferably be coned to about 45 deg., or 90 deg. included. Strictly it should be machined to a " Schiele " curve, but that would be very much gilding the lily in such a small size!

Fig. 51 shows the " Tangye " governor, an excellent and essentially simple device. It is admirably suited to the smaller and simpler type of model stationary engine (and to portable and traction engines too). In full size practice it must have been applied literally to thousands of engines.

Where, as in this case, a balanced piston type of throttle valve is used, it does not need to be a perfect fit in its sleeve, as its function is to regulate the steam supply, not entirely to cut it off, though as shown in the drawing it is actually doing so, the sort of thing which would only happen in an emergency if for any reason the entire load were suddenly removed from the engine and it " ran away ". This is a type to be thoroughly recommended.

In passing, with throttling governors in particular, it was very

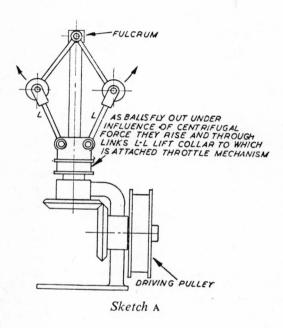

Sketch A

The oldest form of Watt governor is illustrated in the accompanying sketch A and is usually driven by means of a belt or rope from the main crankshaft through bevel gearing.

This type usually too, operates a throttle valve in the steam supply pipe as also shown in the sketch B. If the engine speed tends to increase, the governor balls, under the influence of centrifugal force, tend to fly farther out and in so doing they lift the sliding collar by means of the lower links, which in turn through its lever and shaft connections partially closes the throttle valve and thus tends to reduce the speed of the engine.

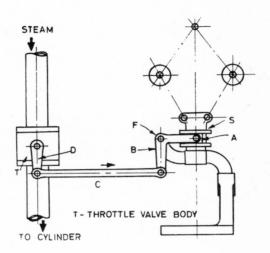

STEAM

F
S
A
B
D
T
C

T - THROTTLE VALVE BODY

TO CYLINDER

Sketch B. *As governor balls speed up, they move outwards, thus raising slider* S *and lifting point* A *on bell-crank lever* B, *which has the effect of drawing the link* C *to the right and moving the lever* D *which is mounted on the butterfly throttle valve spindle, and thus tends to close the valve and reduce the steam supply to the cylinder*

Governors divide into two main types: (*a*) Those governing by throttling the steam supply, and (*b*) those governing by altering the cut-off of steam to the cylinder. The latter can be sub-divided into (1) those operating to move the main eccentric and so alter the travel or setting of the main valve, and (2) those operating upon a separate shut-off valve; the latter affect the timing of the cut-off point only and do not affect any changes in exhaust and compression periods as does (1).

usual practice to fit an arm with a loose jockey pulley at its outer end which was supported by the belt or rope driving the governor. The other end was connected to the governor throttle valve spindle. If the belt or rope broke, the arm dropped and closed the throttle valve, thus preventing any untoward racing of the engine due to the governor being put out of action.

Fig. 53 shows a governor, generally similar to the Hartnell in principle, but applied directly to the crankshaft and arranged to act on a throttle valve. This form was very largely used on high-speed vertical engines, both open and enclosed crankcase types. A guard or casing was generally arranged to enclose it, but in a model this is not really necessary, and it has the drawback that it prevents " the works " being seen. The engine shown in the frontispiece has a governor of this type, but one which includes a detail which is *not* good practice, namely that the controlling spring operates through the shoes on the sliding sleeve, which of course tends to undue friction and wear.

The self-contained spring arrangement shown in Fig. 53 is very much to be preferred as an altogether sounder and more mechanical arrangement. It would be well here to stress the point that in model work provision should always be made for adjusting the controlling springs, whether of the compression or tension type. The governor shown in Fig. 53 is of a variety which has been very largely used on small and medium powered stationary engines and on portable and semi-portable engines too. This is a governor which controls the main eccentric, altering its position in such a way as to vary its travel without altering its angular advance, thus maintaining the lead constant. Fig. 53 shows in diagrammatic form the movement of an eccentric at "*A*" and at "*B*" a pair of eccentrics for a Stephenson gear. The points $X.Y.$ in "*B*" represent the eccentric centres; if either eccentric could conveniently be arranged to move along the path XY or YX, the other could be dispensed with and you would have a reversible and variable cut-off gear, in effect very similar in action to the Stephenson, but without its variable lead characteristic. As a matter of fact many gears working on this principle have been made, but mechanical difficulties have always been considerable.

The eccentric shown at "*A*" is caused by the governor, to move through a path very closely approximating to XZ. When at X the valve has maximum travel, at Z minimum travel, and consequently a much earlier cut-off.

The horizontal engine shown on Plate 7 has a governor gear of this type.

During the heyday of the reciprocating steam engine, literally scores, if not hundreds of mechanisms have been invented to achieve the desired movement of the eccentric. The actual movement of the eccentric was achieved in two different ways, (1) as indicated in Fig. 53 with the eccentric embodied on a pivoted arm, and (2) by fitting a second smaller eccentric within the body of the main eccentric and arranging that the governor revolved the two eccentrics in *opposite directions* thus in effect causing the eccentric proper to move through a path closely approximating to *XZ*, Fig. 53. The results are the same whichever scheme is adopted: the swinging arm arrangement is perhaps the simpler and certainly the easier to understand, whilst the double eccentric arrangement is perhaps the smoother working.

For those interested in this latter form there is an article by Muncaster in Vol. XXVI of the *Model Engineer*, pp. 249 *et seq.*, illustrating it in a size applicable to a Stuart-Turner No. 9 horizontal engine (it could equally well be applied to the No. 4 vertical). There are excellent detail and general arrangement drawings included.

Muncaster was not only a very widely experienced mechanical engineer, but a most excellent draughtsman; it is safe to say that in all its long history the *Model Engineer* has never published better drawings than his.

Fig. 53 shows a governor controlling the movement of the main eccentric. Its working is fairly obvious. Under centrifugal force the weights *W.W.* tend to move outwards against the pull of the tension springs, in so doing they cause the bell cranks to turn about their fulcrums and they in turn move the bar *L* to the right carrying the eccentric with it. Actually the mechanism shown is by no means as simple as it might be, but its action is so easy to follow that it was thought well to present it as an example of the type. On this question of simplicity in mechanical design and construction, just as it is true that the man who causes two blades of grass to grow where one grew before, is a benefactor to mankind, so it is equally true that the engineer who can make one component do, with equal efficiency, the work of two, is equally a benefactor of mankind. In my earliest days in the drawing office, I was fortunate enough to work under a chief who was not only an extremely clever engineer, but who took a very real interest in his junior staff. I well remember a piece of advice which he was never tired of repeating. " When you have designed something, no matter how simple, sit back and look at it and think whether it can be still further simplified either in its construction, or from the point of view of the shops, without, of course, interfering with its functional efficiency." That is just as sound advice for the model engineer as for the professional.

Far too many people are far too easily satisfied with their own work; all their birds are fully-fledged swans of immaculate plumage, whilst those of other folk are just dirty ducks.   Any suggestion that *their* designs attain anything less than perfection, let alone the idea that is is possible to improve upon them, causes an immediate and alarming rise in blood pressure.   Never be tempted to offer suggestions to this type if asked for your opinion of his work, they are not wanted and will not be welcome; what is wanted is praise and eulogy, preferably laid on with a trowel!

The governor shown in Fig. 53 (left) is an excellent example of what can be done to simplify a mechanism, as a comparison with Fig. 53 (right) will clearly demonstrate; this is the Westinghouse governor used by the firm on their single acting overhead valve engines, the prototype of so many models.   Geo Westinghouse is best known for his invention of the compressed air brake that bears his name, but he was a very clever and versatile engineer, as well as a superb organizer, and he had a great many useful mechanical inventions to his credit.   Here again the action of the device is fairly obvious. The link T which connects the two weights serves to keep their movements symmetrical and to transfer the power of the right hand weight to the left hand one; it passes behind the link L which actually moves the eccentric and has no connection either with it, or the eccentric, it just happens that as shown in the closed position it passes directly behind the pin joining the link L to the eccentric. As the weights move outwards under centrifugal force the eccentric is drawn to the left thus reducing its travel and hence shortening the cut-off.   This mechanism is so essentially simple that it would be difficult to improve upon it.

For model purposes there is nothing to choose between throttle governing, and expansion governing, it boils down largely to a question of individual choice.   Generally speaking throttle governors present the simpler constructional proposition, but expansion governors are perhaps the more interesting to observe in action.

You pays your money and you takes your choice.   For those model engineers who take pleasure in scheming and designing, governors of all sorts offer an unlimited field for the exercise of mechanical skill and ingenuity.   If anyone has sufficient intelligence to pursue model engineering as a hobby, it is a fair assumption to credit him with well developed reasoning powers and the capacity to exercise them; further, that once beyond the tyro stage, he does not require to have every " i " dotted and every " t " crossed. The attitude that model engineers are a lot of morons, to be discouraged from thinking for themselves and from exercising any sort of individual initiative is insolent presumption, by and large their intelligence is well above average, particularly in their own chosen field.   The mathematics of governor design are not abstruse, but it is felt that they are hardly called for in this book.

Those who desire to go more deeply into the matter will find all the information they require in text books on the steam engine, notably in those covering the last two decades of the 19th century and the first decade of this, a period covering the highest and final development of the reciprocating steam engine. Most of such books are now out of print, but can be found in any good reference library. A number of them are included in the bibliography at the end of this book. Concluding these brief notes on governors it may be said that once the model engineer has passed the " beginner " stage, he should seriously consider fitting some sort of governor to all his future stationary engine models.

CHAPTER 18

MISCELLANEOUS

Lagging ; Splash Guards ; Drain-cocks ; Feed Pumps ; Stop Valves ; Saddle Keys ; Nuts, Bolts, Setscrews and Studs ; Locknuts ; Painting ; Finish ; Forcing Screws

LAGGING

This is a matter frequently neglected in model work, and model locomotives are, in passing, amongst the worst offenders. The heat losses in any small steam engine are very large and it behoves us to do all possible to reduce these as much as we can. Not only should the cylinder and steamchest be encased as completely as possible, but between the casing and the cylinder and steamchest should be inserted a good non-conductor of heat; flannel or wool felt are as good as anything and much better than asbestos, which, though an excellent fire resistor, is *not* a particularly good lagging material.

Soaking the flannel or felt in alum prior to application is advantageous. The outer covering may be of metal or wood. In the former case nothing looks so nice as blued lagging steel, but this is not always easy to come by. Next, I think, comes a *dull* chrome plated finish; personally I think polished brass or copper looks appalling and in any case it is out of character away from fairground plant. If you use wood, wax-polished mahogany or teak strips held by polished brass bands, *not too wide*, looks good, particularly on models of older types of engine, say prior to 1900. You won't *stop* heat leaks by lagging, but you can considerably reduce them. I know the specious old argument about the relatively small fuel consumption of model engines rendering considerations of efficiency unimportant all too well. It seems to me to be the very negation of the spirit of the true model engineer. The true model engineer will not be satisfied until he has it working at the highest efficiency his knowledge, ingenuity, and skill can contrive.

SPLASH GUARDS

For open type engines, either vertical or horizontal, which run at any speed splash guards are, if not a necessity, at least a great convenience and improvement, and they do stop a lot of oil slinging around the place.

Don't, in making this type of splasher overlook the necessity of allowing clearance for the connecting rod big end, as well as for the crank itself. The picture of my little factory engine, Plate 7, shows a splash guard of the crank-race type, made from a piece of polished stainless steel and that of the 2 in. × 2 in. Stuart, Plate 4, shows one with side pieces, clipped to the turned front column. The engine shown on the frontispiece has one similar, but not

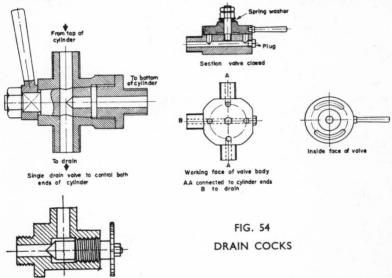

FIG. 54

DRAIN COCKS

shown in the picture; the tapped hole for its retaining stud can be seen quite clearly in the front column. Blued lagging steel with a half-round edging of polished brass or steel looks good as too does a plain polished stainless steel job; again avoid either polished brass or copper; both these, in their place are lovely metals, but their place is *not* cylinder lagging or splash guards except perhaps on the fairground !

Drain Cocks

Cylinders of any size, say, $\frac{3}{4}$ in. bore and upwards should be fitted with drain cocks. These may be of several forms. For simplicity and efficiency you cannot beat the plain screw-down needle type, they never stick, and remain steamtight. Fig. 54 (lower left) shows one, and the picture of my little factory engine shows a couple of the type fitted.

Ordinary taper-plug cocks can be, and frequently are, used and so long as the plugs are initially a good fit and are kept well lubricated with graphite grease they will function satisfactorily, if they show any tendency to leak, remove the plugs at once and re-grind them, using fine glass powder or rotten-stone, *not* on any account emery or carborundum, which will bed itself in and continue to grind for ever after. If leakage is allowed to persist, it will more likely than not lead to a seized-up plug.

Finally, there is the flat faced valve taking care of both ends of the cylinder, see Fig. 54 (top right). It will be seen that with the valve in the central position the drain outlet is sealed by the bridge-piece *B* of the valve, move the handle 30 deg. in either direction and both drain ports are put into communication with the outlet. The valve is pivoted about a central spindle and held to its face by a strong spring washer and lock-nuts. Such a valve is shown in the picture of my reversing mill engine, Plate 6. Of course, any of these drain cocks may be fitted with unions and waste pipes.

FEED PUMPS

The drawings Fig. 55, show typical feed pumps, a horizontal short stroke pump and a vertical ditto, and also a long stroke horizontal pump suitable for driving directly from the engine cross-head.

Short stroke pumps are almost always driven by eccentrics in the smaller types of stationary engines, frequently from a valve gear eccentric, thus making it serve a double purpose. Occasionally in the smaller horizontal engine the feed pump was incorporated in the valve driving mechanism, either between eccentric and cylinder, in which case it acted as an intermediate guide to the valve spindle, which had of course to be carried through a packed gland behind the pump ram, or behind the steam chest, in which case the pump ram was operated by an extension of the valve spindle which of course necessitated a packed gland at the back of the steam chest.

In the foregoing remarks, the " front " of the engine is regarded as the crankshaft end. Tangye's of Birmingham frequently used these latter methods of operating their feed pumps.

In marine work the pumps were usually driven by rockers giving a reduced stroke. A common arrangement was to group the air pump, circulating pump, boiler feed pump, and bilge pump (the two latter usually being alike) in a single unit driven by a pair of rocker arms operated by the L.P. gudgeon pin. A similar arrangement was frequently found in big horizontal mill engines (without the bilge pump!) but in these cases the rocker arm took the form of a bell crank, the pumps being vertical as in marine work.

Fig. 55, centre left, shows an arrangement of a feed pump frequently applied to model locomotives in the past, in which a reduced passage connects barrel to valve chamber and a spigot is made on the end of the plunger " to reduce clearance ".   In at least one case this spigot was dimensioned so as to be of the same nominal diameter as the bore of the hole in question.   As water is, for practical purposes, incompressible, just what was supposed to happen to the water trapped in the barrel between ram and spigot, history does not relate, but it must have caused fun and games.   The whole idea is crude and quite unnecessary and the arrangements shown in Fig. 55 are in every way better, both functionally and from a constructional point of view as it allows a straight through bore for the barrel which is a much simpler machining proposition, and has no countervailing drawbacks. As a side comment on the fatuous " spigot " idea its originator later produced a design for a long-stroke pump, with the valve chambers about the middle of the barrel, and a clearance volume *greater than the swept capacity of the ram!*   A truly noteworthy example of a complete lack of "consistency ".

A most important point in pump design is to provide suction and delivery pipes of ample size, for short stroke pumps these pipes should not be less in clear bore than half the diameter of the ram, and for long stroke pumps equal the ram diameter. Sharp bends should be avoided like the plague.

For working model feed pumps, stainless steel ball valves are strongly recommended and their lift should be restricted to a maximum figure of $\frac{1}{8}$ the diameter of the ball.   The White steam car, which had pumps driven at engine speed, had $\frac{5}{8}$ in. diameter bronze ball valves, and these were restricted to a lift of only 1/32 in. Anything more resulted in rapid deterioration of the balls and their seats and a lot of most objectionable noise.   Of course, these pumps worked at high speed, up to 1,500-1,750 r.p.m. and at 600 lb. per sq. in. pressure; at least that was the pressure in the boiler, the pressure in the pumps and feed line was almost certainly much higher.   An air vessel on the delivery side helps to reduce hydraulic shocks and to smooth out the delivery.   If fitted, such a vessel should have a *minimum* capacity equal to 4 times that of the pump.   It is essential too that means be provided for draining the vessel at intervals, which means that a plug should be fitted at the top to allow ingress of air.   Air is slightly soluble in water, and, unless drained, the air vessel will in course of time become full of water and so completely fail to fulfil its function.   It is hardly necessary to point out that all joints must be carefully made and kept airtight.

A separate check valve should always be fitted on the feedwater

delivery line close to the boiler.   If a feedwater-heater is used, it is
well to fit an additional check valve on the pump side of the heater.

   It is not possible to lay down hard and fast rules for pump sizes,
as these will vary over a wide range dependent upon the size and
efficiency of the engine concerned, and to some extent upon the
speed at which the pump operates.

   Generally speaking the smaller the engine, the larger, in proportion to the engine cylinder will the pump require to be, for the
simple reason that, *on broad principles*, the smaller the engine the
greater will be its thermal losses and in consequence its demand for
feedwater.

   As a very rough guide, engines with cylinders up to about ¾ in.
bore will require a pump having a swept capacity of about 1/80th
of that of the steam cylinder.   For slightly larger engines this figure
may be reduced to 1/100 steam cylinder capacity.   If in doubt,
err on the large side, but don't overdo it, as an outsize pump mops
up quite a lot of power.   Regulation should always be done on the

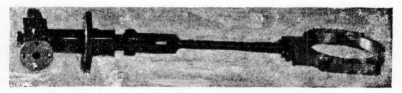

Plate 10.   Glandless Feed Pump with guided ram

delivery side, do not on any account attempt to throttle the intake.
The bypass valve should be connected to the delivery line, as close
as convenient to the pump, and a screw-down type of valve is far
preferable to a plug cock.   When fully open the valve should have
a clearway through equal in area to that of the delivery pipe.

   As to constructional materials, gunmetal for pump bodies,
stainless steel for rams or plungers, stainless steel balls for valves.
Large pumps may have their bodies made from cast iron, but in
such case neck rings and glands should be in gunmetal.   In special
cases it is sometimes desirable to do away with the stuffing box,
make the ram a really good fit in the barrel and fix two leather
cup rings at its inner end.   See Fig. 65.

   This form of construction has the advantage that it makes possible
the guiding of the ram thus relieving the barrel of side pressure and
liability to wear.

   This form of construction provides for a most efficient pump,
but it does require really accurate workmanship.

   Note that the form of valve seating shown in Fig. 55, right, much to be preferred to the more usual type shown in the middle. This latter form is much more liable to trap grit and foreign matter under the ball and thus interfere with its functioning; so far as my information goes, it was introduced to the model world by the late **Hy** Greenly more than fifty years ago.   One final word; when seating ball valves, do the job properly as indicated in Fig. 55.   This method ensures that the ball is struck square and central with its seat, if it is not so struck the seat will be distorted and no amount

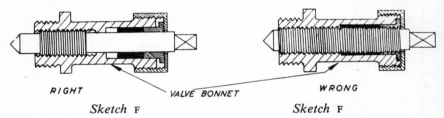

RIGHT   WRONG
VALVE BONNET

Sketch F   *Sketch* F

of subsequent bashing will serve to correct it, you will have the alternatives of recutting the seat, or putting up with a permanently leaking valve.

STOP VALVES

Whilst the plug-cock type of valve may be used for this purpose, it has, in my opinion, nothing to recommend it.   It is not a sensitive regulating device (and if used at very small openings is apt to " cut " and develop leakage !) and unless kept carefully greased very apt to stick too.

The screw-down valve, either of the " straight-through " or " angle " type is the ideal thing. It is simple and sensitive, can be maintained steamtight and requires very little maintenance.   In larger sizes it should have a valve made separate from the spindle and floatingly attached thereto.

The spindle should be so arranged that the screwed portion does *not* pass through the packing, see sketches FF.

The free passage through the valve should not be less than 1/12 of the piston area, if the engine is expected to work really hard; for light running, however, much smaller areas are quite satisfactory.

SADDLE KEYS

Cutting small keyways in shafts unless you have milling equipment is not easy, but there is an alternative, and that is to use a " saddle " key.   Quite apart from the fact that a saddle key looks well and if properly fitted functions well, it possesses certain advantages.

It avoids the necessity for a keyway in the shaft and also it is adjustable around the shaft, hence it is ideal for eccentrics, as it allows of accurate final setting before locking in place.

Strangely enough, it seems either to be unknown to, or at least unused by, model engineers as a whole. It is most important that the concave side of a saddle key really conforms to the diameter of the shaft on which it sits; unless it does this it will not be satisfactory. I make mine as follows. First I take a piece of round steel large enough for the purpose, chuck it in the three-jaw and bore it accurately to a diameter equal to that of the shaft to which the key is in due course to be fitted. I then turn the outside to an *included* taper of $1\frac{1}{2}$ deg. as sketch G.

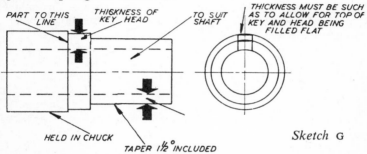

Sketch G

When parted off, key blanks can be cut out with a fine hacksaw as required and the upper surfaces filed flat and the sides squared off. Note, a key of this type is *top* and *bottom* fitting, and should be an *easy fit* sideways.

Nuts, Bolts, Setscrews, and Studs

I have been accused of being a fanatic about the use of slot-headed screws in models, and people who only half read what I write have frequently rushed into print to scarify me and to point out that slot headed screws are used in full sized practice. I am as well aware of that fact as the next man and I have never criticised their use in proper places, as for instance for holding footplating in place, or fixing cylinder lagging, to mention but two legitimate and correct uses.

Slot headed screws are *not* used in full sized practice for holding on cylinder covers, for retaining connecting rods on crankpins, for joint pins in valve gears, neither do you find countersunk headed screws *in shear* used to fasten cylinders to frames as is common in certain forms of model locomotive design, and is rank bad practice, even if it does " work "; they too are apt to " work " (loose) ! Those are the things I criticise, the use of slot headed screws in the *wrong* places under *wrong* conditions and you can see them at every model engineering exhibition in the country.

On the other hand many models are spoilt by having hexagon-headed screws, bolts and nuts of grossly over-scale size. The smallest hexagon steel normally obtainable is ⅛ in. across the flats, and for really small work this is too large.* Most commercial bolts and nuts are made (for model work) from hexagon steel with a dimension across the flats equal to twice the diameter of the shank or tapped hole and this gives a clumsy head or nut.

One-eighth inch across the flats is O.K. for 8-B.A. nuts and bolts or 7-B.A. setscrews.

Frequently, too, nuts and bolt heads are made too deep; the head of a bolt or setscrew should not be more than 0·875 of the diameter of the shank, whilst a nut may be of a thickness equal to diameter of tapped hole, locknuts three-fifths of this figure.

Generally, up to 5/32 in. use material as nearly as possible one-and-a-half diameter of bolt over flats, thus ⅛ in. = 3/16 in. across flats, 5/32 in. = ¼ in. across flats (this is a plus figure, but you are unlikely to obtain hexagon steel 15/64 in. across flats). In special cases this ratio can be reduced for bolt heads but not for nuts.

Use studs where possible in places such as you would expect to find them in full size practice, as cylinder and steamchest cover fastenings, etc.

PRESSURE IS TAKEN
UP BY TOP NUT

Sketch H

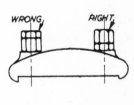

Sketch H

Finally, locknuts; nine times out of ten if locknuts *are* used in a model (and they are rare enough anyhow) they are wrongly fitted, the *thick* one should be outside, it takes the weight ! See sketches HH.

Locknuts should be used on bearing caps, connecting rod big and little ends (where bolts are used) eccentric straps, etc.

Properly applied their use adds realism and value to any model and in a model expected to do hard and continuous work they are a definite necessity unless substituted by some other form of nut-locking device.

* Small hexagon stock is now readily available.—K.N.H.

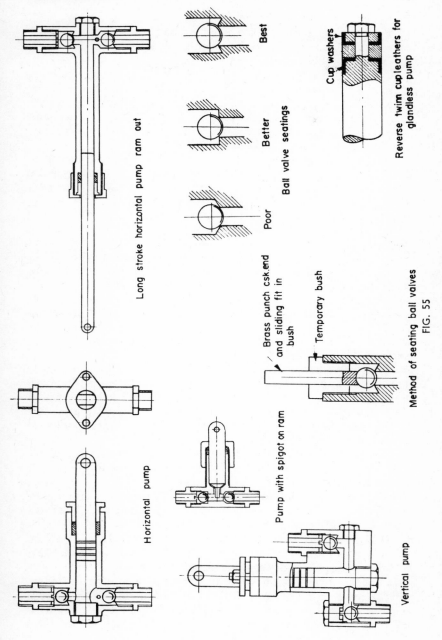

Long stroke horizontal pump ram out

Best

Better

Ball valve seatings

Poor

Reverse twim cup leathers for glandless pump

Cup washers

Horizontal pump

Pump with spigot on ram

Brass punch csk. end and sliding fit in bush

Temporary bush

Method of seating ball valves

FIG. 55

Vertical pump

PAINTING

Probably more models are spoilt by bad painting than by any other single fault, and all too frequently this goes for models which otherwise display unexceptionable workmanship.

I suspect that this arises from a very human failing; painting is usually the very last job and human nature being what it is, the builder is as likely as not getting a little tired of the job and is most anxious to see it finished, in consequence he tends both to rush and to scamp the job, and if there is one thing you cannot do with painting and get away with it, it is to rush it.

First of all, every surface to be painted should be as smooth as possible and before applying any paint or filler, surfaces must be thoroughly cleaned with petrol, turps, or some other de-greaser; after this keep your fingers off at all costs; some people have sticky fingers (in the literal sense !) and leave their fingerprints on any metal work they touch; just look at a model which has been at an exhibition for a few days, suitably protected [?] of course, by notices " Please do not touch." Its bright parts, forwarded to the C.I.D., would serve to track down, by the finger-print system, 90 per cent. of the small boys in the district, plus probably at least 50 per cent. of their fathers !

Rough castings (which should be filed first to remove the worst roughness) should be treated with a coat of filling paint and after this has set hard it should be rubbed down thoroughly. Where surfaces are really bad, two coats of filler may be necessary.

Blowholes should, of course, be " stopped " with metal cement previous to applying the filler. When the filler coat is satisfactory, apply a priming coat of a flat paint of a neutral colour, such as grey, and when set, rub down lightly. Then apply up to five coats of the final colour, each quite thin, and allow each to set really hard before giving a light rub down. Finally, give a coat of clear varnish. All this work should be done in a room as free from dust as possible and it is good practice to protect the model by some form of cover whilst each coat hardens off.

The real answer to painting problems is threefold, cleanliness, multiplicity of *thin* coats of paint, and extreme patience. The extra time spent will be well repaid in the final result.

Brass is a notoriously bad " holding " material for paint; if you can get it sandblasted (very lightly) this provides a splendid key, but if you have this done, don't forget first of all to protect any machined surfaces with surgical adhesive tape. An excellent alternative is to make up a solution of perchlorate of iron about 4 oz. to the pint of water, and dip the brass-work into it. This is an etching medium and will leave a beautiful matt surface ideal for painting. A very little experimenting with a bit of scrap brass will indicate the time the brass should be submerged. Wash thoroughly in cold or hot water, allow to dry, *and keep your fingers off after* !

As to colour schemes, various shades of green have always been popular for stationary engines and of these nothing looks better than a medium olive green; avoid grass green or pastel shades of green like the plague !

Royal blue looks extremely well, whilst the fine old Midland Railway red is equally effective. Such shades as the old North British brown or the L.B.S.C.R. yellow I regard as too horrible for words as applied to stationary engines (other than hot potato engines !).

FINISH

And this is " Finis " too. Bright surfaces should be well and cleanly finished, but not necessarily highly polished, a direct draw finish with medium fine emery cloth looks well. Always remove sharp corners from your work with a fine file, used as a draw-file *along* the corner, but don't round the corner off, only just remove the knife-edge of it.

Finally, don't round flat surfaces—keep them *flat*. Don't above all, try to cover up poor finish by applying a high polish over an improperly prepared basic surface. " Highly polished, deeply scratched," is a term of contempt applied by old hands to this procedure ; don't let it apply to your work.

FORCING SCREWS

Just one other item which, whilst not being directly concerned with finish, has a considerable bearing on maintaining a good finish in good condition.

Cylinder covers and steam-chest covers (in fact, any form of bolted, studded or set-screwed cover making a pressure-tight joint) should always be provided with two or more tapped holes through which forcing screws may be put to start the cover and break the joint when the bolts, studs, etc., have been removed. Usually, it is convenient to place such tapped holes on the pitch line of the fastening screws, and place them symmetrically with regard to the area of the cover, so far as size is concerned they may be the same as or slightly smaller than the holding bolts or studs.

CHAPTER 19

TESTING MODEL ENGINES

IT IS fair to assume that most model engineers who have got past the pure " working to instructions " stage are interested in the actual performance of which their engines are capable. There are two main methods used in ascertaining the performance and power output of full sized reciprocating steam engines. One is by ascertaining the " brake " horse power, which gives the actual effective horse power that the engine can transmit to the machines or apparatus that it is required to drive. This method is only suitable for comparatively small powers unless an expensive and somewhat complicated hydraulic dynamometer is available. It is, however, eminently suitable for application to models. The second method is to take indicator diagrams, which in effect show the actual power developed by the piston but take no account of the power lost by internal friction of piston, piston rod, valve, valve gear and motion work, i.e. crosshead, connecting rod main bearings, etc. Depending on the size and type of engine in question the brake horse power is likely to be anything from 75 per cent. to 85 per cent. of the indicated horse power. Whilst it would be rash to say that it would be impossible to " indicate " a model steam engine, it is safe to say that the practical difficulties involved are so great as to put it beyond the resources of the average model engineer, this is a pity, because an indicator diagram can give a very accurate record of what is actually taking place in the cylinder, and most valuable information on the effects of changes in valve proportions and setting, matters about which, as things stand, we are almost totally ignorant.

There is, however, a fairly simple alternative which, whilst not giving anything like the information obtainable from an indicator diagram, does give us a very good idea of the average M.E.P. in the cylinder, and if taken in conjunction with the r.p.m. a fairly accurate assessment of the indicated horse power. The apparatus involved is quite simple and well within the capacity of any reasonably skilled model engineer to make. It is fully described later in this chapter.

It will be obvious that turbines cannot be " indicated " and furthermore, the powers developed are usually so large as to put the brake h.p. method quite out of court.

The practice with turbines therefore is to rate them by " shaft horse power ".

This is obtained as follows. When torque is applied to a shaft, providing there is a resistance to its turning, it twists to a greater or lesser degree depending of course on its size, the amount of torque applied and the resistance. This applies to any size of shaft whether it is $\frac{1}{16}$ in. diameter or two feet diameter. If you want to demonstrate this fact take a piece of silver steel, say $\frac{1}{8}$ in. diameter and a foot long, fasten a small lathe carrier or other form of clamp to one end, grip the other end in the vice and twist the carrier.

You will find that you can get quite a few degrees of twist without putting a permanent " set " into the steel by putting such a strain upon it as will exceed its elastic limit. It may be hard to believe that exactly the same thing takes place in the huge tail shafts of the " Queen Elizabeth ", but it is a fact that it does. By measuring this twisting or deflection and counting the revolutions the horse-power being exerted can be calculated. The apparatus involved is complicated and costly and in the form used in full size can be ruled out of court for our purposes. However, the late Hy Greenly designed a piece of apparatus, working on the same principle, which is not difficult to make, and which can be used to obtain the shaft horse-power developed by the engine to be tested. Many years ago I made up such a piece of apparatus, closely following Greenly's design. This was not made for testing model engines, but for checking the output of fractional horse-power motors required to drive sub-standard cine projectors. It functioned perfectly satisfactorily, and proved an infallible means of sorting out any motor whose performance was below standard.

This apparatus too is described later on in this chapter.

Reverting to brake horse-power testing, this is usually done by a rig-up of the type shown in Fig. 56. "A " shows a clasp type of brake and "B " a band brake. Both these have been widely used, but for the model engineer involve quite a lot of work and very careful setting up. A further disadvantage is that the braked wheel, usually the flywheel, is very liable to overheat if the trial is continued for any length of time.

In the early 1900s a device was patented by a Mr. Sellers for simple brake testing which appears to be ideal from the model engineer's standpoint (the patent has of course long since run out).

It is illustrated in Fig. 57 and its inherent simplicity is at once apparent both as to construction and application. It consists of a long steel frame with a hinge about $\frac{1}{4}$ of its length from one end. On this frame is mounted a four wheeled trolley, the wheels being flanged and running on the upper edges of the frame members.

On the upper surface of this trolley is mounted a block of wood
with a smooth flat upper surface. In the original apparatus this
was of elm thoroughly impregnated with belt dressing, but any
hard wood would be suitable; I would suggest particularly lignum
vitae or teak on account of their inherent oily nature.

To one end of the trolley is attached a spring balance. Note
particularly that in use the flywheel to which it is applied must
turn in the direction of the arrow, i.e. so that it tends to drag the
trolley *away* from the spring balance. Pressure between wood
brake block and wheel is obtained by placing weights on the outer
(left hand) end of the frame. The calculation involved to ascertain
the brake horse-power is extremely simple and could be carried out
by any intelligent child of twelve years of age, and even by a self-
styled " Practical Man ". All that is necessary is to measure the
diameter of the flywheel, take its R.P.M. and note the reading of the
spring balance.

Thus: Diameter of flywheel 6 in.
R.P.M. 770.
Balance reading 4½ lb.

Then a 6 in. diameter flywheel having a circumference of 19 in.
as near as makes no matter = 1·58 ft.

The formula is: Pull on Balance in pounds, multiplied by speed
of rim of flywheel in ft. per min., divided by 33,000 = B.H.P.

$$\text{Thus:} \qquad \frac{4·5 \times (1·58 \times 770)}{33,000} = ·166 \text{ B.H.P.} = \tfrac{1}{6} \text{ B.H.P.}$$

Just in case any beginner wants to know what the 33,000 is,
this represents 33,000 ft. lb. of work per min., which is the accepted
figure for 1 horse-power.

In the example given above the engine is exerting 5,474·7 ft. lb.
per min. = $\frac{1}{.6}$ B.H.P. Incidentally this power is probably rather more
than a man of average physique can exert over any prolonged period,
the usually accepted figure for this being about ⅛ H.P.

Turning now to the model engineers substitute for Indicating,
the apparatus to be used was invented many years ago by the late
Professor William Ripper of Sheffield University, incidentally the
author of one of the best text books on the steam engine with which
I am acquainted. This apparatus is illustrated in Fig. 58, which is
based on the illustration and description in Ripper's own book. As
the drawing shows, this is really a very simple piece of apparatus
and well within the competence of any reasonably experienced
model engineer to make, in fact the only rather fiddling bit of work
in it is the little double beat valve *E* which perforce must be made in
two parts and assembled in place.

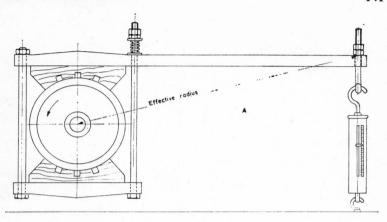

Clasp dynamometer brake

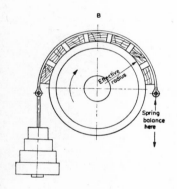

FIG. 56.

BAND BRAKE DYNAMOMETER

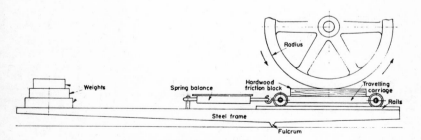

FIG. 57. SELLERS' DYNAMOMETER

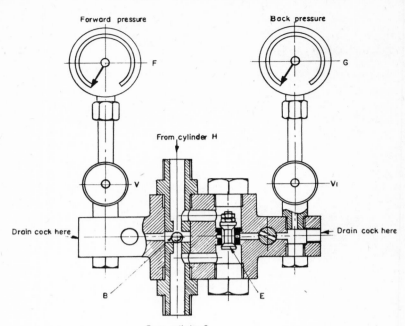

FIG. 58. RIPPER'S MEAN PRESSURE INDICATOR

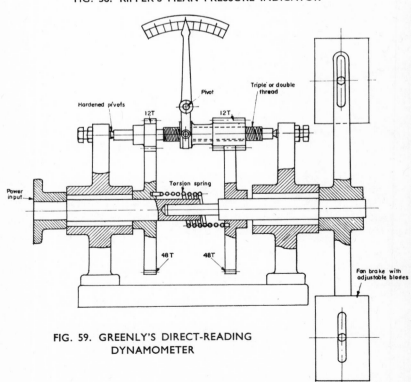

FIG. 59. GREENLY'S DIRECT-READING
DYNAMOMETER

The apparatus works as follows: *H* and *C* are connected to opposite ends of the cylinder. Let us assume that steam is entering the end of the cylinder connected to *H*. Acting on top of the double beat valve *E* it will close its upper end and at the same time open it to the connection *C* and thus to the other end of the cylinder. It will also close the ball valve *B* to *C* and will have access to the pressure gauge *F*. When the piston reaches the end of its stroke, the slide valve will have opened the end of the cylinder connected to *H* to exhaust and be admitting steam to the end connected to *C*. Pressure will rise in this line closing *E* to gauge *G* and the ball valve between *C* and *H* and thus allowing the inlet steam access to gauge *F* as before and the exhaust to gauge *G*, also as before.

Thus gauge *F* is always registering steam pressure behind the piston and gauge *G* exhaust pressure in front of it.

The two valves *V* and *V1* are needle valves to adjust the inlets to their respective gauges, and are so set as to prevent the readings fluctuating. We thus obtain a steady reading on gauge *F* of the average pressure behind the piston, doing useful work and ditto on gauge *G* of the exhaust pressure retarding the piston. Subtracting the latter from the former gives us the M.E.P., i.e. the average useful pressure capable of doing work.

If we now record the number of strokes per minute (and presuming we know the bore and stroke of the engine) all we have to do to obtain a close approximation to the indicated horse-power it is developing is to carry out a simple calculation.

The formula is:

$$\frac{P \times L \times A \times N}{33,000} = \text{I.H.P.}$$

and must be familiar to most readers.

P = M.E.P. (in this case as derived above)
L = Stroke in *feet*
A = Area of piston in *sq. in.*
N = Number of strokes

Thus: P = 66 lb. per sq. in. L = 2 in. or $\frac{1}{6}$ ft. A = 3·14 sq. in. N = 1,500 (= 750 R.P.M.)

Then:

$$\frac{66 \times 1 \times 3\cdot14 \times 1,500}{6 \times 33,000} = \text{I.H.P.}$$

$$= \frac{3\cdot14}{2} = 1\cdot57 \text{ I.H.P.}$$

The figures given are of course purely arbitrary and in fact the

66 lb. per sq. in. M.E.P. would call for a pretty high boiler pressure probably well over 100 lb. per sq. in. Incidentally they illustrate what quite considerable powers a comparatively small engine can develop, the B.H.P. in the above case would probably be between 1 and 1¼. It also emphasises the vital necessity for providing such engines with ample bearing and wearing surfaces and continuous lubrication if they are not to wear themselves out in a very short time. The actual detail layout of the apparatus can be varied to suit individual circumstances, but every effort should be made to keep it as compact as possible, whilst the connections to the cylinder ends should be as short and direct as possible. The pressure gauges themselves should be carefully checked against either a dead-weight testing set or a large gauge of known accuracy. The type of gauge having a centre-mounted hand is to be preferred and having a more open scale.

Considering finally the Greenly apparatus, this is illustrated in Fig. 59. A is the input end, and to avoid troubles in lining up, a short cardan shaft with a flexible coupling of the Hardy Spicer type is arranged between engine shaft and the dynamometer, for that is what the apparatus is.

The input shaft proper finishes beyond the first gear wheel, but the extension shaft which carries the absorption fan, which provides the load is spigoted to it and connected to it by a coil spring. Note particularly that the spring should be so arranged that when the apparatus is working, the tendency is for the spring to be wound up. Thus far we have a simple fan dynamometer.

Now for the indicating apparatus. A lay shaft is mounted parallel to the main shaft and to one end of it is fixed a gear wheel, which gears with one mounted on the input shaft. A gear similar in size to the one on the input shaft is mounted on the extension shaft and this too mates with a wheel on the lay shaft. This wheel is not fixed to the lay shaft, but mounted on a threaded portion of it, and carries a sleeve with a grooved collar, which by means of shoes controls an indicator needle. This wheel too has a face broader than the one that drives it, so that it may travel lengthways without coming out of engagement.

Now let us see what happens when power is applied to the input shaft; via the spring this turns the fan shaft. The lay shaft is driven by the fixed gears and the screw mounted gear is also driven at the same speed by the gear on the fan shaft.

The fan however sets up a resistance to rotation, which causes the fan shaft to lag behind the input shaft to an extent until the winding-up of the spring balances the resistance of the fan shaft. This results in the floating gear on the lay shaft being turned relative to the shaft by an amount depending upon the lag between input shaft and fan shaft; in doing this it moves endways along the screw and so operates the pointer. Now it will be obvious that the apparatus can be calibrated in such a way that the scale over which the pointer moves indicates foot pounds, inch pounds, kilogram centimetres or any other convenient unit. The calibration is probably the most troublesome part of the job. In the machine which I made it was done by means of an electric motor of known efficiency with an accurate and sensitive ammeter. A small easily driven tachometer was operated from a pulley on the input shaft by means of a spring belt. First of all the apparatus was driven *without the fan*, at the approximate speed at which the motors to be tested operated and the position of the pointer on its scale noted and marked zero, the amperage taken by the driving motor being noted. The fan was then mounted and its paddles adjusted until, at the required operating speed the additional amperage taken by the driving motor corresponded to the minimum required power output of the motors to be tested and the position of the pointer marked on the scale. Motors which failed to bring the pointer to this position were thrown out and returned to the makers.

A few words on the construction of the unit. All moving parts should be kept as light as possible to reduce inertia. The input shaft and fan shaft were mounted on Skeflco self-aligning ball bearings, whilst the lay shaft was mounted on hardened centres, the gear ratios were about 3 to 1 in order to gain an increased displacement endways of the floating gear, for any given lag of the fan shaft behind the input shaft.

The thread on which the floating gear was mounted was triple, 24 to the inch, in effect $\frac{1}{8}$ in. pitch, again to ensure a reasonable amount of end movement to operate the pointer. Some experimenting had to be done to obtain a suitable sized spring, and arrangements should be made in the detail design and construction of the apparatus to make the fitting of varying sizes of spring reasonably quick and easy.

Admittedly there is a great deal of work involved in making and calibrating such a piece of apparatus as this, but it can, used intelligently, provide a great deal of very useful information, and it is, in my opinion a very worth while thing to make, by the type of model engineer who wants hard facts as opposed to airy, and all too often inaccurate generalities.

This apparatus was described in the *Model Engineer* 56 years ago, the one I made around 1930 is the only one I have knowledge of, which is not very high testimony to the enterprise of model engineers, or tribute to their enthusiasm for the experimental side of their craft!

To deal adequately with the subject of testing model engines would require a whole book, at least as long as this one, and in this short chapter it has only been possible to deal with the matter in very general terms and to describe certain reasonably simple apparatus which can be used for the purpose, all of which is of a practical type and has been tried out.

On the general question of engine testing and indeed of any sort of experimental work the following points are worth bearing in mind. If testing is worth while, and it surely is, it is worth doing as throughly as possible. First, be sure that all your apparatus is in good condition and properly adjusted. Secondly never work on your own, always enlist the assistance of one or two friends who know something about steam engines to act as observers, recorders and assessors. Thirdly repeat your trials several times, and if the results of any one trial are widely out of line with the rest, discard them and repeat one or two more tests. Fourthly, keep conditions as stable as you possible can for each series of tests. Fifthly never alter more than one condition at a time; this is a matter of the most vital importance if the results of your tests are to have any real value. By all means carry out rough trials on your own, to get an idea of the trend of things, but having done that don't, repeat *don't*, rush into print and claim you have " proved " something; if you do all you will have " proved " is that you don't know the first thing about genuine worthwhile testing and (or) experimental work. In the *Model Engineer* for April 26 and May 10, 1906, there was published a most excellent paper, read by the late H. H. Harrison before the Society of Model and Experimental Engineers, which is well worth reading by those interested in the subject, the paper was very well illustrated and contains a great deal of valuable information. In much more recent times E. T. Westbury and the late John Latta have made many valuable contributions on the subject of B.H.P. testing and the apparatus involved; the fact that these contributions referred to I.C. Engines in no way invalidates their usefulness and interest to those seeking information on the practical testing of model steam engines.

The well-worn proverb to the effect that a thing worth doing is worth doing well, applies with particular force to testing and experimental work of all sorts, and those who are not prepared, not only to subscribe to this dictum, but wholeheartedly to act up to it, had best leave this sort of work alone.

CHAPTER 20

A TWIN CYLINDER NON-CONDENSING
LAUNCH ENGINE

SOME MAY query what this design is doing in a book about " Model "
engines, as it is not a model at all, but a small power marine engine
intended for practical work.

It is suitable for driving a boat on river or fresh-water lake;
the size of the boat would depend very largely on its type, a heavily
built boat of 14-16 ft., a light fine lined river boat up to 20 ft. long.
The design is included because the construction of the engine falls
well within the capacity of any reasonably competent model engineer
having a back-geared lathe of $3\frac{1}{2}''$ centre or above; it was got out
for a friend who wanted such an engine for river work.

The basic idea was to produce an engine which would be relatively simple to construct, call for a minimum of simple pattern-
making and utilise easily obtainable materials.

Cylinder patterns are usually the most troublesome to make,
owing to the rather awkward coreboxes required for the ports and
passages, and to get over this the design incorporates Messrs. Stuart
Turner's standard $2\frac{1}{4}'' \times 2''$ cylinders, which can be obtained at quite
reasonable prices, and as all who have experience of this firm's work
will know are of sound design and first rate easily machinable
material.

The structural features of the engine are made from standard
bright rolled mild steel sections obtainable from any steel stockists.
Only few and simple patterns apart from the cylinders are required,
well within the capacity of any " wood-butcher ".

A geared down (1 to 3) pump is included for boiler feed, but this
is entirely self contained, and if other boiler-feeding means are available or preferred, such as a donkey pump or an injector, this can be
omitted without in any way affecting the design. The main bearings
are of the plain bushed, ring oiling type, and being of large size will
have a long running life.

The valve gear is one which deserves to be better known, the
Dendy-Marshall which was invented by a barrister of that name

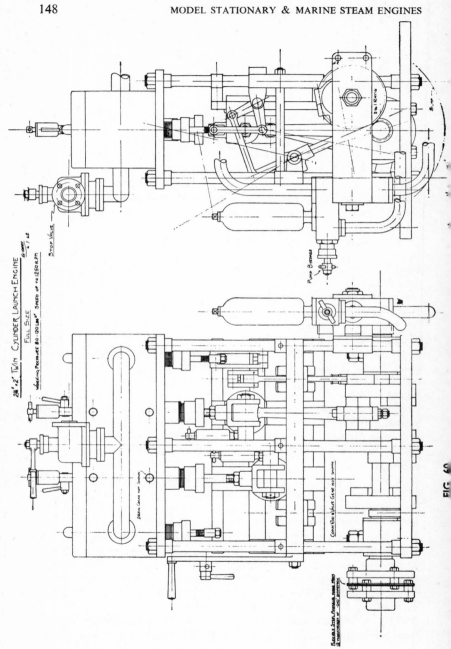

2¼" × 2" TWIN CYLINDER LAUNCH ENGINE

FULL SIZE

WORKING PRESSURE 80-120 LBS/□" SPEED UP TO 1250 R.P.M.

STOP VALVE

PUMP BYPASS

DRAIN COCKS NOT SHOWN

CONN. ROD & VALVE GEAR NOT SHOWN

FLEXIBLE STERN ADAPTOR TAKE PIPE

FIG. 60

about 1913. Although a barrister by profession, Mr. Dendy-Marshall was a very clever engineer and he must have been one of the very few outsiders ever to have had a locomotive embodying his ideas built for their own use by a British Railway, and the old L.N.W.R. and that, certainly not a line notable for accepting ideas from outsiders. The feature of this engine, which was a four cylinder one, was the very ingenious use of a single piston valve to distribute the steam to a pair of cylinders, one inside and one outside.

A description of this engine, together with detail drawings of the cylinders and valves, is to be found in " *The Engineer* " for 20-6-13. However, to revert to the Dendy-Marshall valve gear, this basically is a rearranged form of the Hackworth gear, with the eccentric rod set diagonally to the vertical of the engine, and utilising a curved slide instead of the straight slide used by Hackworth, the final drive being transmitted by a bell crank.

Those familiar with valve gears will note a similarity between this gear and the Strong and Southern valve gears, but both these use a swinging link in place of the slide.

The advantage of the Dendy-Marshall is that by using a curved slide, two points are gained: (a) the gear is much more stable in its working plane, both the gears mentioned suffered from what was known as " side-slap " when worn, a thing that cannot eventuate with the slide, and (b) the radius of the slide can be designed to give the most accurate valve events, in the Strong and Southern gears, physical and constructional limitations make it necessary to use a link much shorter than is desirable from a functional standpoint. Anyhow the Dendy-Marshall gear is simple, robust and gives an excellent steam distribution.

Incidentally it can be used with equal facility to drive valves at the side, in front of, or behind the cylinders; in our case the side drive is utilised as this worked out most satisfactorily from the mechanical point of view. The baseplate and the top-plate which carries the cylinders are made from Bright Rolled steel plate, in its natural condition whilst the engine framing is made up from similar material in square and flat section. The crankshaft can be made from the solid bar, a method only to be recommended for those possessing a fairly hefty power-driven lathe, or alternatively it may be built up on the forced fit principle allowing an " interference " of .001″ per inch dia. of the spigots. Joints should be pegged by round dowels, forced into longitudinal holes half in the web and half in the spigot. Properly carried out this makes a thoroughly sound job and incidentally is much more economical in material as compared with a crankshaft machined from the solid. The connecting rods are rather longer, in proportion to the stroke, than is usual in launch engines, as this tends towards sweeter running and reduces the loading and wear on crossheads and guides. Lubrication of crosshead and slide, little end and big end is taken care of by a large lubricator mounted directly on the little end gudgeon pin, the connecting rod being drilled through to allow the oil to get to the big end. Oil cups are fitted to the cylinder covers, but if superheated steam is used, as it is recommended that it should be, the addition of a mechanical lubricator feeding into the steam supply line *between* the throttle valve and the distributing pipe is very strongly recommended together with the use of a good class high-superheat cylinder oil. The throttle valve is of the disc type and will give sensitive control; a screwdown valve should be placed in the steam line, close to the boiler. As the hulls of small boats, particularly timber built hulls, inevitably tend to " work " to some extent, a flexible coupling is provided; this drives a short intermediate shaft with a similar flexible coupling at its after end driving the tail-shaft proper at the thrust block. The latter can be of the simple multiple-collar type, or of the double thrust ball type. The latter is the more efficient but the former is generally safer, as it is very difficult in a small boat to make certain that water can never get to the thrust block, and if it does, goodbye to ball-bearings.

Throughout, bearing surfaces are very much on the generous side and the engine can be run with steam up to 125 lb. per sq. inch pressure with anything up to 150° F. superheat and at any speed up to 1,250 R.P.M.

Propeller sizes will depend largely on the type of hull, the working pressure and the desired speed of rotation. Much the best policy in this connection is to consult a reputable firm who specialise in propellers, giving them all the relevant data and following their recommendations.

As to boiler capacity, this again will vary with type of boiler selected and to some extent with the method of firing. Oil firing with either a totally enclosed regenerative type bunsen burner or a Lune Valley type white-flame burner is strongly recommended. With a watertube boiler of the Yarrow or Bolsover Express type, a heating surface of 10-12 sq. ft. should be sufficient. With a vertical multi-tubular boiler this should be increased to 18-20 sq. ft., whilst with a well designed " Scotch " marine boiler, fired with good steam coal 15 sq. ft. should be all right. In all cases, superheaters should be regarded as additional, the figures quoted being for evaporative surface.

The addition of a feedwater heater would improve thermal efficiency, if well designed possibly by as much as 10%.

BIBLIOGRAPHY

MODEL ENGINEERING, H. Greenly. *Cassell.*

MODEL MECHANICAL ENGINEERING, E. Steel. *Cassell.*

MODEL POWER BOATS, E. W. Hobbs. *Cassell.*

MODEL LOCOMOTIVE VALVE GEARS, Evans *M.A.P.*

WALSCHAERTS VALVE GEARS, H. Greenly. *M.A.P.*

THE STEAM ENGINE, Perry. *Macmillan.*

ELEMENTARY MANUAL ON HEAT ENGINES, Jamieson, *Griffin.*

SLIDE VALVES & VALVE GEARING, Youngson. *Munro.*

THE STEAM ENGINE, 2 Vols., D. K. Clark. *Blackie.*

VALVES & VALVE GEARS, Vol. 1, H. de R. Furman. *John Wiley.*

STEAM ENGINE THEORY & PRACTICE, Ripper.

THE STEAM ENGINE & OTHER HEAT ENGINES, Ewing.

THE MARINE STEAM ENGINE, Sennett and Oram.

THE ENGINEERS' HANDBOOK, Hutton.

A TEXT BOOK OF MECHANICAL ENGINEERING, Lineham.

EARLY EDITIONS OF KEMPE'S ENGINEERS HANDBOOK.

EARLY EDITIONS OF MECHANICAL WORLD POCKET BOOK.

In addition an enormous number of articles has appeared in MODEL ENGINEER *over the past years and the back numbers will be found to be a treasure house of information on and designs for model stationary and marine engines of all sorts, The* MODEL ENGINEER *and a number of other companies publish blue-prints for such engines, Castings can be obtained from Reeves, Bonds, Kennions, Stuart Turner, etc.*

INDEX